A Terrible Village Poisoning

HANNAH HENDY

CANELO CRIME

First published in the United Kingdom in 2023 by

Canelo
Unit 9, 5th Floor
Cargo Works, 1–2 Hatfields
London SE1 9PG
United Kingdom

A CIP catalogue record for this book is available from the British Library.

Print ISBN 978 1 80032 653 8
Ebook ISBN 978 1 80032 652 1

Cover design by Ami Smithson

Look for more great books at www.canelo.co

Printed and bound in Great Britain by Clays Ltd, Elcograf S.p.A.

1

For Liliya, Maxym and Reuben. Some of my favourite niece and nephews!

Chapter One

'Please tell me we're at least on the right road, Clem,' Margery demanded as she gripped the steering wheel tight, squinting through the rain as it hammered onto the windscreen. 'Gosh, we really couldn't have picked a worse day to leave for holiday, could we?'

'You can't be serious; it's just a spot of rain!' Clementine scoffed from the passenger seat, where she was wrestling with a large paper map. 'It's not as bad as that day the vending machine broke and we couldn't get our crisps after work, is it? Or the time Ceri-Ann set your eyebrows on fire trying to wax them.'

Margery sighed, but she had to admit, it was not as bad as drawing your eyebrows on every morning. She tried to concentrate on the road. They had left the motorway and were on the dual carriageway, finally nearing their destination. Well, they would be if Clementine could start paying attention to the map. She had refused to bring the GPS with them, saying she couldn't trust something that knew where they were all the time, which she had said while uploading a destination-tagged post onto Facebook on her phone. Margery was kicking herself for letting her leave it in their kitchen, still in the box. She had vaguely known how to get there. It had all been plain sailing – until they hit the last big services on the motorway, anyway, and since then she'd been lost.

'What's the town called again?' Margery asked nervously, peering at road signs as they zoomed past them. Clementine turned the map around, frowning.

'Well...ahh...I'm not entirely sure. Something-on-the-something or by-the-sea. Clumpton-on-the-Wibble, maybe?'

'Well, can you ask your phone?'

Clementine rolled her eyes, but pulled her phone out of her pocket anyway. Fellow dinner lady Ceri-Ann had given Clementine a few lessons on phone management in the very few moments of downtime they had at work, and Clementine was getting much better at using it. The photographs she took were usually in focus now, and it was rare her thumb made an appearance at the edge of the shot. She could even send a text message. There had been a time when she was so bad at using the phone keyboard that she would only send one dot for yes and two dots for no. Woe betide you if you asked a rhetorical question. What with the computer lessons at the library that Margery kept dragging them along to, they were practically computer scientists now.

'No can do,' she said, turning the phone screen to Margery's face. Margery batted it away so she could keep the car on the road. 'No signal. Don't worry, though, I'm sure it's around here somewhere; I'll know it when I see it!'

Margery rolled her eyes. Clementine was always knowing things when she saw them, which usually ended with them being completely lost. Especially as neither of them had ever been to St Martin's-on-the-Water before. They usually spent their summer holidays off work sitting in the garden on the deckchairs that lived in the shed the rest of the year, after Clementine had removed the spiders from them.

After a very long stretch where Margery continued to drive straight, occasionally looking over to Clementine in worry, and Clementine busied herself with fiddling with the buttons of the radio, they finally came to a sign Clementine recognised.

'Turn off here, Margery!' she said, clapping her hands in glee, sending the map flying off her lap, where it balled itself up into an unsalvageable pile. 'That sign is for the hotel! The Boar's Head.'

Clementine was right. She pulled off the road and the car bounced along the country lane, the small wheels of the Nissan Micra not quite up to the task. The signs were easy to follow now she had found them and soon they were driving up to an old stone building and around the back into a large car park, narrowly missing hitting a woman in the purple waxed coat pruning the shrubs at the front of the hotel.

The wind whipping around Margery's head was very distracting as they clambered out of the car, and she felt glad she had remembered to pack her good rain-coat. The sky above did not look promising at all. It was much too dark for a summer's afternoon; the clouds had knitted together to become one, threatening to spill at any moment.

Still, Margery couldn't help but feel a sudden burst of excitement, even as another gust of wind slammed the door shut. Two blissful weeks on holiday with her wife. Lucky them. They wouldn't let a bit of rain dampen their spirits – or the hen party and wedding food they had been roped into organising for their deputy head, Rose Smith. Next week, Margery's entire team of Education

Centre Nourishment Consultants – who all preferred to be called dinner ladies, except Clementine, who enjoyed the awkward stumbling nature of their full title – were going to join them from Dewstow. Together they were going to throw Rose a lovely afternoon tea in the garden of her holiday home nearby, with crisps, cake and all sorts of other suitable accoutrements. Then two days later she was going to marry Mr Barrow, Summerview Secondary School's headmaster and their boss, in the nearby church, before returning to her garden for a seated wedding breakfast in the marquee. If the weather ever calmed down, that was.

Margery had never seen Rose's house or grounds, but their fellow dinner lady Gloria, who had, assured her that both were big enough for all invited.

'We're quite high up here, aren't we?' Clementine shouted over the wind, as they stared over the fields that started at the back of the car park. They ran on and on as far as the eye could see. Right at the end, if she squinted, Margery thought she might be able to imagine that the line of dark blue on the horizon was the sea. From the Google Maps search she had attempted before their journey, she knew that St Martin's-on-the-Water was quite literally on the water, but the little village had no beach. Instead, it was set over a few miles of sharp cliffs looking over at the little seaside town of Merrowpool. Margery took a deep breath in, enjoying the clean, fresh air as it billowed around her.

Neither woman had ever been here before, but they had heard nothing but good things about St Martin's-on-the-Water from Rose, who had returned every summer since she had been a child. Margery couldn't wait to explore the tiny village and possibly even drive over to

Merrowpool beach tomorrow, though the weather forecast was still not looking fantastic. She took one more deep breath and then turned and walked to the car to help Clementine take their things inside. A relaxing afternoon was most certainly in order after all that driving.

—

'Well,' Clementine said, with more than a hint of trepidation in her voice as she stepped up to the counter and rang the bell. 'I'm sure it'll be fine for a few nights. We'll go out during the day anyway.'

Margery put down her bag and surveyed the reception. It had seemed okay online. The price was absurdly cheap, even for a budget hotel, especially as it included breakfast. She realised now that the photographs on the website must have been very old indeed. The wooden panels lining the hall were a bit cracked and the curtains were musty, and the layer of dust on all the furniture in the dark, cramped reception was particularly jarring. Margery wished briefly that they could just put their things back in the car and head home, but she knew Rose would be livid if they did.

Hopefully they could get a few good week of rest days in before Rose demanded their presence for the organisation of her hen do. Margery wished that she had decided to do what most second-time brides do and have a small and meaningful affair, but it was not to be. Every time Rose talked about it, the event seemed to grow larger and larger. It had really begun to stress Margery out when they had still been at work, and she had all her kitchen manager duties to perform as well as Rose's long list of demands for buffets and ice sculptures. Now that they were on holiday time it was less overwhelming, although she had still filled three A4 notepads with Rose's catering demands. Seren, another of Margery's catering team and Rose's best friend, was not coping particularly well with being Rose's maid of honour. Now she was less stressed, Margery felt it right to try and take some of the burden from her.

'Hello,' a young man said cheerily as he appeared from a back room behind the counter, his sudden appearance and pale skin giving him a ghostly visage for a second before he stepped forward. 'Can I help you?'

'We booked a room online,' Margery said, taking her purse out of her bag so she could show him her driving licence.

'Oh, did you? I didn't know we had another booking.' He ran his hand through his short blonde hair as he sat behind the counter and flipped through the diary on the desk. 'We're quite busy at the moment.'

'Are you?' Margery asked.

'Oh yes,' he said, gesturing with his brow to the window looking out at the silent single-lane country road outside. 'A car went by earlier.' He paused in thought. 'Oh, though I suppose that might have been your car.'

'Oh no!' Clementine said. 'But I'm sure I paid a deposit. I'm sure I have a booking confirmation somewhere.'

'Really?' He frowned, tapping at the open diary page with a pencil. Margery could see that the pages were mostly empty. 'Oh actually…that's you, is it?' He pointed to the page. 'Margery and Clementine Butcher-Baker, also known as the dinner lady detectives?'

'Yes…er…that's us.' Margery rolled her eyes at the memory of Clementine booking the hotel and including their nickname.

'I suppose we do have one room, especially as you've booked.' He sighed and gave them a form to fill in. Clementine placed her bag on the floor and began to rummage around in it for a pen.

'Oh hello!' came a cheery voice from behind them. 'Finally, some guests to check in. Welcome! Calm down, Rupert, you daft thing.'

Margery spun round to see who the voice belonged to. The large man beamed at her as he made his way through the front door with great difficulty, huffing and puffing and being dragged along by the springer spaniel on the lead. He stopped to catch his breath. His cheeks were red with exertion, and he was dripping sweat down his gilet. The thin, greying strands on his head were swept back on his skull, and the overhead light in the reception shone through it. Slightly concerning to Margery was the shotgun resting over his shoulder, although it was unhinged, and she could see that it was not loaded. She had not seen many guns before, though you occasionally did if you went for a walk in the countryside surrounding their home of Dewstow, but she didn't think she could ever feel at ease with one.

'Hello, Dad, hello, Rupert.' The young man behind the desk smiled at the dog as it ran over and jumped up excitedly. He bent to stroke Rupert's ears and then looked at the older man, his brow furrowed in concern. 'Are you all right?'

'Fine, fine, stop pestering me.' The older man puffed, pulling a handkerchief out of a pocket in his utility trousers. 'Just checking in, ladies? I trust Thomas is treating you well?'

Margery muttered in the affirmative as the dog bounded over to her in interest.

'Yes, we're staying.' Margery nodded. 'We're just having a week away before our friend's hen party at the end of next week.'

'Oh, well. I hope the wind calms down for you,' he said, dabbing at his face. It didn't do much good. He was just smearing the sweat around like Vaseline. 'Weather's terrible. Even the grouse aren't coming out – haven't shot a thing all morning. Glorious twelfth indeed. I've got a group of Americans coming next week; they'll be lucky if they get to kill anything at this rate.'

'Quite, quite,' Clementine said, finally pulling a pen from her bag, standing back upright and smiling at the man. He stared at her for a long moment, his mouth hanging open. Clementine's own face fell into crumpled confusion. She and Margery exchanged a look. The man with the gun had gone almost white. He staggered backward and leaned against the wall as if it were the only thing holding him up. The younger man, Thomas, looked between them both with his eyebrows raised.

'Is everything okay?' Clementine asked. Her voice was polite, but Margery could hear her confusion.

'Yes, of course! Everything is perfectly all right, thank you.' The man waved his hands at them dismissively. 'I'll let you and your sister get on. The name's Colin, Colin Warrell. I'm the owner, so let me know if you have any issues,' he said brightly. The shotgun on his shoulder swung as he turned to leave, much more quickly than he'd arrived, nearly stumbling over his own feet in his urgency to get away from them. His ears were slightly too big for his round face, and his mouth was framed by the scruffy, greying goatee. He had obviously been dark-haired before time had taken the pigment out of it. He was tall, but strange in stature because of his beer belly;

Margery imagined his spine must look like a twisted-up coat hanger. There was the chance he might have been better-looking in his youth, but Margery doubted it purely on the sight of his dirty yellow fingernails.

'Oh, we aren't sisters,' Margery said instinctively, wishing she hadn't said anything as soon as the words had left her mouth. 'We're married.'

'Oh,' Colin said, going even more red-faced and turning to look at them both again with a new gaze. 'Well, nothing wrong with that! No, nothing wrong with that. Have a good stay, do make sure you come down for dinner...' He mumbled something under his breath before realising they were still staring at him and then he turned to the dog again. 'Come along, Rupert.'

He dragged the dog away and up the stairs. Margery felt a sinking feeling in her stomach. She found herself wishing that they had stayed elsewhere.

–

They had changed into evening wear, but nothing particularly smart. Before they had arrived, Margery had worried when packing her bag that they would slightly underdressed for dinner at the hotel and she had packed a nicer sundress than usual to wear. Clementine wasn't much better in her faded cord dress and best cardigan, but it would have to do. They hadn't brought loads with them in the first place, and they were saving their best outfits for Rose's hen do, which loomed perilously on the calendar in Margery's brain. Anyway, the room had not raised her hopes for a sophisticated dining room, what with its lumpy bed and peeling wallpaper. She was sure they'd be lucky if a few spiders didn't drop onto them during the night from the cobwebs layering the ceiling. Margery wished they had their own kitchen to make dinner in, but the terrible weather had confined them to the hotel. Great dollops of rain splattered against the bedroom window and after the drive neither of them could face running out to the car and then trying to find somewhere else dry to eat. Maybe tomorrow evening they would leave the village entirely and drive into the nearby town to have fish and chips instead, if it was dry enough by then. She tucked a piece of grey hair behind her own ear as she passed her reflection in the mirror in the hotel hallway. Clementine was already racing ahead as per usual, turning to smile at Margery as they reached the dining room.

There were very few guests. A table of elderly patrons sat at a table across the room, chatting quietly as they looked at the wine list; two older men and a woman, all dressed in dinner wear, made Margery self-conscious about her plain dress. More than that, the man sitting next to the dark-haired black woman was wearing full civic regalia. Margery wondered what on earth the lord mayor of St Martin's-on-the-Water was doing eating at the hotel, or why such a small village even had a lord mayor in the first place. The dining room looked as though it had not been dusted for quite some time, let alone decorated. Cobwebs hung from each corner of the wood-panelled walls. Margery wondered for a moment whether they had accidentally gone backward in time. A bored-looking woman behind the bar looked up from her book as they entered and Margery recognised her as the gardener she had nearly careened the car into.

'Table for two?' she called. Margery and Clementine nodded in the affirmative and she got up from the stool begrudgingly, pottering over to them with a laminated menu in hand.

'You've picked a good night for it,' she said as she led them to a table; 'Today is the day we get the fish delivered so it'll be quite nice. We've also got a cheese trolley!'

She gestured over to a dusty-looking trolley in the corner of the room. Margery decided not to go for the cheese course; the trolley looked like it hadn't been touched for several years. She dreaded to imagine the state of the shrivelled old cheeses underneath the frayed tablecloth draped over it. The woman handed them each a menu with a well-manicured hand and Margery decided instantly that she would go for the chicken. Or possibly something vegetarian to be safe.

'I'm Emily, by the way.' She smiled at them for the first time. 'I'm Colin's partner; I think you met him earlier? Well, fiancée actually.' Emily held out her left hand grandly, narrowly avoiding impaling Clementine in the eye with the huge diamond, so big and glittery that it was almost grotesque in nature.

'Nice to meet you,' Margery said. Emily continued to swish her ring finger around in front of them both. 'Congratulations. That's a lovely ring.' It put the modest wedding band she wore that had once belonged to Clementine's grandmother to shame.

'Thank you.' Emily looked at it admiringly. 'The wedding isn't till next summer, but I just can't help showing it off!'

She need not have bothered; the ring was so enormous she could have seen it glinting from the next room, Margery thought. Then chastised herself for her own nastiness. She could hear her mother, who was always in her head one way or another, reminding her to be nice.

Emily seemed awfully young for Colin as well. Barely older than his son, if Margery was judging correctly, though she supposed looks could be deceiving.

'Very exciting,' Clementine said. 'We're actually planning a wedding for a good friend. Well, we're doing all the catering anyway.'

'Good friend' was going a bit far when talking about Summerview school's drama teacher and deputy head, Rose Smith, Margery thought. 'Barely tolerated acquaintance' was much more like it. They had all become much closer after Rose had hired them to clear her name before the Christmas holidays, but since then they had settled back into a testy truce.

'Ooh, are you?' Emily smiled. 'Colin would have me doing our catering if I let him. What would you like to drink? I've got red wine, white wine?'

'Just a bottle of white please,' Margery said, sensing they wouldn't get any further choice beyond the colour.

'No worries, you sit tight, and I'll get your drinks.' Emily sauntered back off to the bar.

The décor in the dining room was quite warming, but the unnecessary log fire that was burning on the far side of the room was even more so. Margery could feel sweat begin to drip down her forehead. She fanned herself gently with her menu as she squinted over at Clementine's. None of the dishes would have been out of place if they had accidentally gone back in time forty years; the entire menu was peppered with out-of-date classics.

Colin Warrell entered from the swing doors behind the bar and went straight over to the table of two older men and the woman Margery had seen when they arrived, and shook the mayor's hand with gusto. She could not hear what he was saying, but whatever it was must have been very humorous. Both men were around Colin's age, though maybe the mayor was slightly younger, and Margery wondered idly how he knew them. He clapped the man with the neat white beard on the back and wandered over to the bar to greet Emily, who fawned over him as she poured him a whisky. Colin joined the table and sat down with them.

Emily left through an adjoining swing door behind the bar. Margery assumed it went to the kitchen as she arrived back in short time with three plates of food precariously balanced in her arms. She set them down in front of the three at the table. Margery strained her eyes to see what their plates looked like. The menu did not fill her with much confidence. The two men took a bite of their own meals, then swapped plates and took another. Then they laughed, evidently deciding they preferred the other's food better. The woman rolled her eyes at their antics.

'Good evening, ladies.' A man approached their table from behind them. Margery had not seen him arrive. His black hair was balding on top but otherwise he looked in quite good shape for a much older gentleman; he must have been at least in his early seventies. 'You're the detect-ives, yes? The dinner ladies? Thomas told me about you.'

His voice was very smooth, with a hint of an Indian accent. Margery could imagine him being a good radio host.

'Yes, we're the dinner lady detectives,' Clementine piped up, before Margery could stop her. 'And you are?'

'George, George Kale,' he said softly, one of his weatherworn hands resting on their table; the knuckles and joints looked swollen and sore. He looked as though he was in two minds about something. 'Are you really detectives?' He looked them up and down like he did not believe it for a moment.

'Yes,' Margery replied mildly. 'Well, we've solved a few bits and bobs.'

'Oh right,' he said finally, seemingly aggrieved. 'Well, lovely to have you stay. If you need anything for your room let me know. I do maintenance and gardening around here; I've been here since Mr Warrell opened it, so I know lots of lovely walks in the area too, if that's your thing.'

'Thank you.' Clementine chuckled, pointing to her own slightly overweight stomach. 'But we aren't big walkers.'

'Then I'll let you enjoy your evening,' George said, smiling. 'If you change your mind, I live in the little caravan behind the hotel, through the car park. You can't miss it; come and knock for me.' George disappeared as quickly as he had arrived, exiting through the kitchen doors.

'Are you ready to order?' Emily was back, plonking the bottle of wine down next to them and then pulling out a notepad from her apron pocket.

'Oh yes,' Clementine said, her glasses slipping down her nose as she looked back down at the menu. 'Prawn cocktail to start for me please and, er…chicken chasseur, I suppose.'

'Fantastic,' Emily said, scribbling away with her pen. 'And for you?'

Margery had begun to read her choice out loud when there was a sudden shout from across the room, and a rasping sound. The mayor had stopped eating and was clutching his throat. For a moment Margery assumed he was choking and she briefly ran through the steps of the

Heimlich manoeuvre in her head, but then he turned around and she could see that his eyes were red and swelling and his tongue had grown much too big for his throat. The white-haired man leaped from his seat and was trying to calm the mayor as he clawed at his own throat, his nails leaving red marks as they scraped at his skin, the chains around his neck getting in the way like he was a fish caught under an anchor as it dragged him down.

Emily, who had been frozen in shock, seemed to reanimate and she rushed to the bar and picked up the phone, jabbing at it with her long, manicured nails. The mayor crumpled to the floor, his eyes wide with terror, and the woman who had been sitting next to him screamed and screamed.

Chapter Two

The man's name had been Nathan Jenkins, Nath to his friends. He had been in his early forties, much too young to end up dead on the floor of a rundown hotel. The paramedics had not asked for his name when they had arrived – everyone in town knew who Merrowpool's lord mayor was – but the out-of-town coroner had asked for it when they came to collect the body.

Police from the nearest town over had arrived and briefly interviewed them all, and Margery had heard herself answering questions as her brain raced at a million miles an hour but she had no recollection of what she had said. As soon as they had been allowed to go, they had gone back up to their room and decided immediately that they should leave. Margery and Clementine had given the officers on duty their onward address and left the hotel with hurriedly packed bags in the direction of Rose's house. They both felt terribly squeamish about staying in a room directly above where someone had died, and died in a horrible way too. Margery could see him clawing at his throat every time she closed her eyes. She had no idea how she was going to sleep tonight, though her eyes burned with tiredness. The clock high on the kitchen wall read half eleven; it was much too far past her bedtime for her liking.

'What was the name of the hotel again?' Seren asked kindly, pouring Margery another brandy. She took the glass with grateful fingers. 'The Boar?'

'The Boar's Head, you said, didn't you?' Rose said. Margery and Clementine nodded in unison. 'Terrible place anyway. I didn't think something like this could happen, though.'

'At least it wasn't boar-ing.' Clementine smiled weakly at her own joke, but she was clutching her own glass of sherry tightly to keep her hands from shaking. 'You should have seen his face. There was a man with him who did CPR for ages, but he was long dead by the time the ambulance arrived.'

'The nearest hospital is in Treliske,' Rose said, flipping her well-groomed silver bob behind her ears. 'It's almost twenty miles away.'

'He didn't take long to die,' Margery said quietly, unable to look anyone in the eye. 'Even if the ambulance was coming from next door, I doubt he'd have had much of a chance.'

They were sitting at the big kitchen table in Rose's old farmhouse, which was as large as Gloria had said it would be. Rose had called it her 'little country getaway' when she had mentioned it in the past. No wonder she had fought so hard to keep it from her ex-husband in their divorce, Margery thought. It was a beautiful house, filled with flagstone floors and original fireplaces. It had taken her breath away when it appeared on the horizon as they had driven down the long, narrow driveway and parked up in the huge front garden, even in the dim light of dusk and with the events of the evening weighing heavily on her mind. It rather reminded her of Rose's mother's house in Dewstow, though she had not been there often. She wondered if that was how she had come into possession of such a place.

'Nathan Jenkins.' Rose stroked her chin. 'I feel like I've heard his name before.'

'It sounds very estate agent-y, doesn't it?' Clementine said. 'Are you sure he hasn't sold you another country pile?' Rose rolled her eyes. Clementine had been making little jokes about the size of her house or oohing about the kitchen Aga since they had arrived half an hour before, and Margery knew her well enough to know that she was trying to hide how upset she was with humour. It was not really working. Margery was glad that Clementine had remembered her phone so they could call ahead and let Rose know they were coming, because they would have never found the house without her direction. Even knowing the address had not been a great help, with how far off the beaten track it was. Rose had made them both a cup of tea and some toast. Margery had been hungry before they had gone down to dinner at the hotel, but now she could not imagine eating again.

'He was the mayor of Merrowpool,' Margery said. Rose 'ahhed' immediately, finally able to place him in her mind.

'Yes, St Martin's isn't big enough to have a mayor, really,' Rose said, sloshing the liquid in her glass. 'He's mayor for both. He's got an office here as well, in the library with all the other council places.'

'What should we do now?' Margery asked, looking to Clementine in concern. 'We can't go back there; I don't think I can, really.'

Clementine sighed, twirling the empty brandy glass between her fingertips. 'I don't think I can either. That poor, poor man. Could we just stay here, Rose? We were due to come anyway next week, weren't we?'

'Yes.' Rose nodded. 'Not a problem, but you'll have to be up in the attic room. It's a bit draughty in all this rain. You don't mind, do you? Failing that, I've got a very nice eight-man tent you're welcome to borrow if you'd prefer the privacy. There's a campsite down the road. You can walk there from here in five minutes.'

'Of course. When's everyone else coming?' Margery asked quizzically. She hadn't been expecting anyone else till next week at least. The hen wasn't due to start until next Friday. It was going to be a three-day affair and Margery was sure that they had their work cut out for them if they were going to prepare everything in time.

'Some are already here,' Seren piped up excitedly. 'Karen and Sharon are staying at the Butlin's with their kids and husbands, anyway; Gloria and Ceri-Ann are coming tomorrow and they're going to stay here. The headmaster even said he might pop in! Though I did tell him he shouldn't see you in a dress before the wedding—'

'My wedding dress, Seren!' Rose cut her off.

'God, this really will be the event of the year,' Clementine said sarcastically. 'If Mr Barrow turns up, we'll definitely get to listen to some ungodly rock and roll record.'

They all chuckled briefly and then there was a beat. Margery found herself looking down at the table, thinking about the man's face as the realisation had dawned on him that he was going to die. She was fairly sure Clementine was thinking the same.

'I can't believe what we saw tonight,' Clementine said, looking down at her fingernails. 'That poor man.'

Margery nodded. That poor man indeed. 'What a way to go.'

'Did they say he was allergic to anything?' Rose asked, sitting back down at the farmhouse table. 'Didn't he have an epi-pen with him?'

'No.' Margery shook her head, feeling a bit sick as the memory came back to mind. 'His friend was a doctor, and he did everything he could. I don't remember the doctor saying anything about an allergy.'

'Doctor?' Rose said curiously. 'Was his name Dr Bell by any chance? White beard?'

'Maybe? White beard definitely,' Margery said, looking to Clementine, who shrugged back at her. She could not recall all the finer details in any great extent. They had mostly sat there in a stunned silence, watching as the doctor had tried to save the man and Emily had flapped around them on the phone to the ambulance. Colin had joined them in the room and been even more useless than they had; he just seemed to be constantly in the way, even when the paramedics had arrived. Even more so than the woman who had been sitting with them, who had turned out to be Nathan Jenkins's wife. Eventually, Emily had ushered Margery and Clementine out into the reception and away from the chaos, and they had stood in shocked silence listening to the horrible wailing of his wife through the closed dining-room doors.

'Well, Dr Bell is the GP around here,' Rose said in explanation. 'It's only a little village, really, St Martin's. Most of the villagers know him, I suspect. Though most of the village know the mayor too. He does a lot for St Martin's – or he did, I suppose – always opening some summer fete or other. He was a nice man.'

They decided to call it a night. Rose showed them to a huge spare bedroom on the second floor, so large in fact that it had an adjoining sitting room and bathroom. It was not what Margery had been imagining when Rose dismissed it as merely her attic room. If you measured it by square footage, then it almost certainly would have been bigger than Margery and Clementine's entire modest two-bedroom terrace. How Rose could afford the electricity bill on her deputy head salary boggled Margery's brain. She supposed she must have won back most of her family money in the divorce. It had been touch and go for a while that Rose would even be able to keep hold of her slightly smaller house in Dewstow, but it had all worked itself out eventually. They got ready for bed and Margery slipped under the covers while Clementine busied herself in the bathroom.

'Clem, should we have stayed at the hotel?' Margery called to her wife. She heard the tap turn off and there was a moment's pause as she waited for Clementine's answer.

'No, I don't think so.' Clementine emerged into the bedroom, her face slightly damp from where she had washed it, her brow etched in confusion. 'Not after that.'

Margery lay back and looked at the wooden beams running across the ceiling. She hoped with all her might that the horrible thing they had witnessed happening to a stranger would be the last bad thing to happen this holiday.

'Have you seen my handbag, Margery?' Clementine asked, her brow furrowed as she scrambled around in their things. 'Only I could have sworn I had it, but I can't remember seeing it since we left.'

'Is it in the car?' Margery asked thoughtfully. She could not remember seeing it either. It was unusual for Clementine to forget something like that; she was lucky that

Margery always carried a spare asthma inhaler in her own handbag.

'No, I'm sure I didn't…' Clementine shook her head, trailing off, still searching through the pile of their belongings next to the foot of the bed. 'Gosh, I think I know where it is.'

'Where?'

'I think I left it at the hotel.'

'Oh no!' Margery sat up in bed. 'So, we'll have to go back anyway.'

'Yes.' Clementine sighed, giving up her search and joining her on the other side of the comfortable mattress. 'Let's not think about that now, though, shall we? Let's just try and get some sleep. It's not as though they'll be open now, and there will be police everywhere.'

'No, I suppose not,' Margery groaned.

'No. And I think I accidentally stole the room key,' Clementine said sheepishly. 'We need to take it back anyway.'

She clambered in and leaned to the bedside table to turn her bedside lamp off. Margery followed suit, intending to try and sleep. Instead, she found herself staring up at the dark bedroom ceiling for most of the night, the events of the day whirling around in her head.

–

Margery awoke early. There seemed no point in staying in bed any longer. It was almost impossible to drift off, no matter how soft and lovely the bed had been. Rose had definitely not spared any expense on duvet sets, even for guests.

She wandered down to the kitchen, leaving Clementine upstairs still in bed scrolling through Facebook on her phone, and was surprised to find that Rose was already there at the big kitchen table. She was surrounded by papers and was busily typing away at her laptop, working on a tiringly busy-looking spreadsheet. In the middle of the table was a big cafetière of coffee and the empty mug in front of Rose suggested she had already had a few cups.

'Good morning, Mrs Butcher-Baker.' Rose smiled, taking off her glasses and rubbing her eyes. She gestured for Margery to sit down. 'You're up early. Was the room all right?'

Margery sat down opposite her and helped herself to the coffee. 'It was lovely, thank you. I'm just finding it hard to drift off.'

'Ah yes.' Rose nodded. 'Menopause comes for us all.'

'Oh well, no, not that. Just you know, the man dying and…'

'Oh! Right, yes,' Rose said awkwardly, finally looking up from the laptop. 'Well…bad show, that, I suppose.' She blushed and Margery tried not to let her grimace show outwardly. She often felt as though she did not know how to talk to Rose. Rose and Clementine simmered along nicely with jokes that often veered towards the wrong side of rudeness, but Margery wasn't like that as a person. Rose considered her for a moment over her glasses, like she wanted to ask or tell her something, but then she dipped her head down and began to type again. They lapsed into an uncomfortable silence. Margery made herself a cup of coffee and sat watching Rose work.

'Are you doing lesson plans?' she asked eventually to break the uneasy silence that had fallen between them.

'I am.' Rose nodded, not looking up from the computer. 'I know I could just recycle the same ones each year, but I like to keep things fresh.'

Margery felt a glimmer of respect for Rose. She could recycle them indeed. Margery definitely recycled the canteen menu plans, but that was more because there would be a terrible revolt if they didn't put on fish and chips on a Friday, and Margery would be ousted by angry children and staff. Underneath Rose's biting remarks and sleek silver bob, she was in fact a highly respected teacher. Perhaps she was trying even harder than normal this year; it had not been an easy road here. The governors had not been particularly impressed with Rose's relationship with Mr Barrow, the headmaster, and there had been an independent enquiry into their upcoming marriage. It had all worked out, but Margery felt privately that they had both been very lucky to retain their jobs.

'I know of the owner of The Boar's Head, you know, well…I've known of him for a long time,' Rose said, jolting Margery out of her thoughts. 'Colin Warrell is not a very nice man.' She looked up from the laptop and rested her chin on her hands.

'No?' Margery said, helping herself to a spoon of sugar from the pot in the middle of the table.

'No,' Rose said. 'I've heard a lot of bad things, almost too many to tell you in one sitting, but it makes sense that the mayor was there. Mr Warrell likes to have friends in high places from what I've heard. It's such an awful thing to happen.'

'I think so too,' Margery said, resting her head on the palms of her hands wearily. 'Do you know if they were friends before last night?'

'Gosh, you're asking the wrong person, really.' Rose smiled slightly. 'I usually only come here for a week at Christmas and a few weeks in the summer; I split my holidays between here and my chateau in Dormond, you see. I know most of the villagers, though, and my family used to summer here when I was a child, so I'm well versed in most of its history. I know Mr Warrell and the mayor know each other, but to what extent I'm not sure. Dr Bell I know too. Everyone knows him, though; he's the only doctor for miles.'

'Really?' Margery asked. 'Do you know why he'd be at the hotel with the mayor?'

'I'd imagine they're friends.' Rose took her glasses off and rubbed her eyes. 'But like I said, I know most people but not everyone likes me much. Some of them don't like that I own this house, I think because I'm not local. But it was my grandfather's and he left it to me, so I can't get rid of it. It's part of my family history, and you know how little of that I have better than most people. I tend to keep to myself and just chat with the friendlier faces.'

Margery nodded. She did indeed. Rose's birth mother, Caroline, had wanted nothing to do with her and she had been raised by her grandparents. It was a very sore subject for Rose, who had tried for years to regain some connection to her but had been spurned at each opportunity, partly from her mother's insistence on keeping her at arm's length, like she was a pet she had grown tired of. Margery and Clementine had known Caroline very well, having worked under her for years when she was their kitchen manager, and she had never even mentioned having a daughter. Margery had always wondered if some of Rose's ill temper stemmed from being spurned so much.

Rose returned to her work, gently tapping at the computer keyboard, and Margery sipped her coffee and enjoyed the peaceful morning. The sun was rising on the front side of the house and the back kitchen was still cool.

Margery imagined that the farmhouse must be practically freezing in the winter.

'There is one thing,' Rose said, still looking at the computer, 'but it happened so long ago that I just can't see it being relevant now.'

'Well, what is it?' Margery asked. 'I'm sure any information would be helpful to the police; they didn't seem to have any ideas either.'

Rose nodded and opened her mouth to speak. The doorbell chimed, the noise ringing out through the hall and reaching them in the stone-floored kitchen. Margery swung her head towards the sound. She looked back to Rose, who had also looked over in concern, her brow furrowing.

'Are you expecting someone?' Margery asked her. Rose shook her head.

'No,' she said, raising her eyebrows. 'Maybe another uninvited guest? They seem to be descending on us in their droves.' She gave Margery a wry smile, which Margery returned with a chuckle. 'Let me shout Seren to get the door.'

'Shall I go and look?' Margery asked quickly, rather than have Rose scream Seren out of a peaceful slumber at half past six in the morning. She stood without waiting to be told. Rose nodded.

'If it's Gloria then ask her how the cake plan is coming along for the reception,' Rose said, leaving the kitchen as the doorbell chimed again. 'Tell her I don't want any marzipan and if she's planning a fruit cake then she had better think again.'

Her voice trailed off as Margery walked out into the long hallway of the house, wishing she had worn socks as her feet wandered over the cold stone floor. Whoever was at the front door was growing ever more impatient. They had begun to knock heavily, the noise echoing around the room. Margery paused at the big wooden door before pulling it open. She came face to face with two police officers and stepped back with a start, her hand still on the cold door handle.

'Mrs Margery Baker?' the female officer asked, her short blonde hair sticking out of the sides of her peaked cap.

'Butcher-Baker,' Margery corrected. 'Yes.'

'We'd like to have a word with you and your partner.'

Chapter Three

'I don't see how you can suspect us,' Clementine demanded. 'We've barely been in the village ten minutes, how could we have had anything to do with that?'

Detective Penfold was a softly spoken, blonde-haired woman with eyes like a hawk. Currently they were scanning Clementine's face as if looking for some piece of information they had mislaid while Margery looked anxiously to the interview room door as though Seren and Rose might jump in and save them. While it was not the first time they had been questioned about a crime, it was certainly a much more frightening experience than when they had had disagreements with Dewstow's local bumbling police force while solving Summerview school's drama teacher's murder at Christmas, or even the very first time when they had been caught trespassing at the scene of their kitchen manager's murder. For one thing, at least those times Margery had known what crime they had supposedly committed. This time she was not sure what the officers sitting before them were trying to accuse them of.

The tiny room they were in did not make her feel less of a criminal with its carpeted walls and needless amount of plug sockets. The dark-haired male officer who had interviewed them the night before sat next to Detective Penfold opposite them and looked as frightened of her as they did. Margery wondered how on earth a small town like Merrowpool had a detective inspector on staff. Neither the police at Dewstow nor the much bigger neighbouring town of Ittonvale had such a thing at all. It made the hairs on her arms stand up in fright; surely this meant the death could not have been an allergy. No police force in the country would be able to justify using Detective Penfold to solve something so innocent.

'You're both here voluntarily,' Penfold said lightly, though there was a sneer of incredulity behind it. 'We're investigating a man's death. We have to look at every angle.'

'Well, we've told you what we saw,' Clementine said, the wind taken out of her sails momentarily.

'You did.' Her voice was barely a whisper. Margery looked at her face. She was a lot older than she had initially thought. Of course she would have to be to become a detective inspector, but at first glance Margery would have said she was merely in her thirties. But the deep frown lines on her forehead would not appear on anyone more youthful.

'So, we can go?' Clementine asked.

'Just one more thing,' Detective Penfold said, sitting back in her chair and regarding them both carefully. They had been here for at least an hour, maybe even longer, being asked the same questions over and over and made to describe the events of the night before again and again. It was as though the detective thought that one of them would eventually slip up and confess to something, but there was nothing to confess to. Margery was on her last nerve, had been for the last twenty minutes and was trying to stop her hands shaking so badly as she gripped the glass of water in front of her. It was not enough for the young PC next to her to take notes; they were also being recorded on the machine that was whirring on the table next to them. Margery kept eyeing it suspiciously. Almost as suspiciously as Detective Penfold kept eyeing Clementine. Whatever was going on here, Margery did not seem to be their concern at all.

'Why did you leave the hotel?'

'We told you,' Margery finally snapped. 'How many times? We were scared; we had just seen a man die, for Christ's sake!' Clementine did not even remind Margery not to swear. Instead, she nodded adamantly, her grey fringe bouncing as she did so. Detective Penfold finally turned to Margery, as if she had only just remembered that she was there.

'Where is George Kale?'

'How should we know?' Margery snapped, throwing her hands up in exasperation. Detective Penfold put down her pen and tutted. She had already asked them twice if they knew where he was. Margery could barely remember what the hotel's gardener looked like; they certainly didn't know where he was. Detective Penfold didn't look ready to give the line of questioning up. If anything, she looked almost as though she were enjoying herself.

'Why does any of this even matter?' Clementine said. 'We didn't make his food, did we? It wasn't our fault he was allergic to something.'

The room slipped into a terse silence as the officers looked at each other and something passed between them unsaid. Margery fidgeted in her seat uneasily.

'We're proceeding with the theory that Mr Jenkins's death was not an accident,' Detective Penfold said coolly. 'And we are waiting for the post-mortem to confirm.'

Margery and Clementine were stunned into silence. Detective Penfold considered them both again carefully, scrutinising their faces.

Margery's voice felt crackly like an old record when she managed to speak again. 'You think someone killed him? How?'

'That's why we're trying to find Mr Kale.' Detective Penfold clasped her hands together and leaned back in the chair. Margery had finally had enough.

'If you're not going to let us go, then we aren't going to tell you anything more. Not without a solicitor,' she said as firmly as she could muster, hiding her hands under the table so the police officers would not see how much they were shaking.

'You're free to go; you've been free to go this entire time,' Detective Penfold said finally, still eyeing them suspiciously. She had seemed to realise that neither of them knew what she was trying to blame them for. Clementine stood immediately and started to shrug her coat back on. 'But this isn't over yet. Don't leave town.'

'Don't leave...' Clementine stuttered indignantly, turning back to look at the police officers with only one arm in a sleeve, the rest of the coat flapping ridiculously behind her. 'Don't leave town? You can't stop us. We've got two cats at home! And besides, we have to leave town to go back to the village, don't we!'

St Martin's-on-the-Water was so tiny that the police officers had asked them to accompany them to Merrowpool Police Station several miles away. Margery wondered if she should pinch herself. Maybe she would wake up back in their bed in Dewstow to find this had all been a horrible dream. It was not the visit to Merrowpool that she had envisioned; her idea had been more 99 ice creams and sunhats on a sandy beach.

'I don't think you want to find out what we can and can't do,' Penfold said. She smiled but her eyes remained as cold as ice. 'Do you?'

Clementine shook her head as Margery grasped for her handbag under the table. They needed to get out of here; nothing good could come from staying in the small, dark room any longer.

'Here's my number.' Detective Penfold wrote it on a piece of paper and thrust it at them. 'Call me if you suddenly find you have something more to say.'

Clementine took the phone number. Margery tugged on Clementine's arm, and they left the room as fast as they could, Margery barely remembering to grab her coat on the way out.

'What on earth was all that about?' she whispered to Clementine in confusion. 'Why are they looking for George? Do you think he killed the mayor?' Clementine looked as puzzled as she felt, but there was also more than a hint of annoyance there.

'I've got no idea, but I intend to find out,' Clementine said finally as they rounded the corner back into the main reception and the officer let them go.

–

The police officers had said not to leave, but they had mentioned nothing about not going back to the hotel. Besides, they had paid for the whole week; the room was still available for their use.

Margery felt the apprehension building as she drove them up the narrow lane to the old brick building. Rose had told them that this was a terrible idea when she had called to demand why they weren't back at the house yet, which should have been a warning enough.

Margery felt her shoulders slump even though she did not mean for them to, and she kept her foot on the accelerator, the car rolling at a steady pace.

'What's wrong?' Clementine looked over at her.

'It's just…' Margery struggled to put the thoughts in her head into words for a moment. 'I'm getting a bit sick of all this. All these horrible deaths, I mean. It's great when we manage to solve something, but wouldn't it be nicer if no one had died at all? The police seem convinced that this is something worse than an allergy. I don't want us to be sucked into anything again.'

Clementine nodded in understanding. Terrible things did seem to be happening all the time. A few years ago, their lovely, humdrum day-to-day existence had turned into a constant circus. This was the third murder that they had been involved in in less than two years. Margery wondered what they had done to deserve it. It was one thing to always be joking and calling themselves 'the dinner lady detectives', but it was another entirely to live that life.

'What about…' Clementine began gently, placing her hand over Margery's clamped tight around the steering wheel. 'What about if we just do a few more years at the school?'

Margery turned to her in surprise. 'And then what?'

'Retire, of course.' Clementine smiled. 'Get a dog to upset the cats and renew the National Trust membership.'

'Gosh!' Margery laughed. 'I don't know if we'll have enough cash for that, money bags! And what about the school kitchen?'

'What about the kitchen?' Clementine said sincerely. 'They'd be fine; it's only breakfast club and lunches, for God's sake. Not rocket science or hanging patterned wall-paper.'

'Clementine, please do not swear,' Margery teased, beaming at her wife. 'Oh, Clem, do you really mean it? Who would do the mashed potato for the children, though? No one's as good at doing the mash and the mushy peas as you are. And I can't just leave; who would do the ordering?'

'That is true about the mash,' Clementine said, raising an eyebrow. 'But Gloria would take over. She'd be great.'

Margery thought about her second-in-command. Gloria would be a fantastic kitchen manager. She practically ran the rest of the kitchen anyway when Margery was doing the stock take or stopping Clementine from eating all the sprinkles they put on the Friday lunch trifles. Add to that Ceri-Ann becoming much more capable recently. Even Seren was much less a danger to herself and others as time went on under Margery and Gloria's patient guidance. She hadn't had an accident for months, not since she had spilled an entire soup kettle of custard into her own shoes. Luckily it had been cold at the time.

'You're right.' Margery nodded.

'I'm always right,' Clementine said. 'Apart from when I'm not.'

They pulled into the tiny car park, the car tyres flicking water up from the waterlogged ground, pulling up against the fence that led into the fields beyond as they had the afternoon before.

As they got out of the car, her eyes were drawn to movement in the field. Margery could see a caravan, and she could just make out the sight of the door blowing back and forth in the wind.

'Come on.' Clementine grasped for her hand. 'Oh, is that the man's house? The one they're looking for?'

Margery struggled to remember for a moment, watching the door continue to move back and forth, rummaging through the filing cabinet of her brain that kept useless information about cake recipes but remembered no names. 'Yes, I think that's where he said he lived at dinner. I wonder where he's gone?'

'I wonder why they're looking for him,' Clementine said.

They rushed down the reception stairs and out of the building into the glorious fresh air of the car park. Margery took great gulps of it; the air was still thick and muggy from the rain but it was a relief after the stuffiness of the hotel, which had been empty and dusty. The walls had seemed to close in on themselves the longer they stayed inside, though it had only taken Clementine a moment to grab her handbag and then a few minutes more for them to chuck their door key down on the desk with a note to say they were checking out for the week and that they would email for a refund at a more appropriate time. They wandered around the main building and back towards the car in the car park behind.

'This is all very strange,' she said, her fingers tightening over the strap of her own handbag as they marched. Clementine was very quiet and thoughtful, perhaps a little too much so for Margery's liking. 'Where is everyone? You'd expect this place to be crawling with police and forensics teams, wouldn't you?'

'I know,' Clementine said, 'it's like they've all disappeared. But the building was open. Someone must have unlocked the doors this morning.'

Clementine paused, kicking a cigarette butt away from her. 'Is that the kitchen?'

Margery turned to look where Clementine was pointing. She was quite right. The kitchen fire escape was open, a line of police tape running out of it into the car park. It almost looked like it had been ripped down so that someone could push open the door. Surely the police wouldn't have left the hotel without securing it? She felt a chill run down her spine.

'We can't,' she begged Clementine, who had already turned in the direction of the door. Margery knew that she was seconds away from suggesting something mad, like they get themselves involved in an investigation again. 'The police already seem to have their eyes on us for some reason. We can't break into a crime scene, can we? Remember what happened the last time we did that?'

Clementine groaned. 'Yes, we solved a murder.'

'Eventually!' Margery almost shrieked. 'Do you not remember all the trouble we got into before it was solved?'

'Of course I do, but this is all just too odd, Margery.' Clementine shook her head.

'I know,' Margery said. 'I agree. I don't understand the police's sudden interest in us either. It seemed a lot more than just general questioning, didn't it?'

'So, let's just have a look in the kitchen,' Clementine said. Margery rolled her eyes. 'Come on, there's no one here. What's the worst that could happen?'

Margery snorted. Clementine knew perfectly well what the worst that could happen was, but she looked back to the open kitchen door with longing anyway. Margery sighed.

'One quick look?' Clementine said. Margery shook her head but followed her anyway.

They slipped quietly past the police tape and down the short set of stairs. The tape had definitely been torn away from where it had been stuck; there was sticker residue all over the fire escape push handle, though Margery daren't touch anything to confirm her suspicion. Her heart thumped much too fast; if they were caught down here things would not get any better for them. Hopefully the police had already taken what they needed and would not be quick to recheck the kitchen, she thought as they arrived in it, all the while wondering if someone else had already broken in. Clementine pulled her sleeve down over her fingers and turned the light on. The room was filled with the much-too-bright light from the strip bulb above them. It was a tiny kitchen compared to their work canteen and looked even older, if that was possible. All of the school's kitchen equipment was certainly ancient, but it did not look in any way as rundown as the hotel's did. They would never pass their annual health and safety audit with such atrociously cared-for shelving units. She noticed immediately that even the chopping boards were worn. One had a big round ring melted on that she knew from experience came from a saucepan being left on top of it. It was not a good sign if a kitchen could not replace even the least expensive of equipment.

As kitchen manager, Margery took good care of their appliances and she knew Caroline had done the same before her, but she found herself feeling grateful for the yearly checks their ovens had. These looked like they barely worked at all. To make matters worse, the cleanliness left a lot to be desired. There was grease dripping down from the extractor fans above the six set of hobs in the corner, which still had used pans on top. The dishwasher still had a stack of dirty pans underneath it that looked as though they'd been there a good while. On the opposite wall were two microwaves that obviously saw a lot of use, if she were judging by how dirty the handles on the doors were. The police would have had no issues getting fingerprints from them.

Across from the ovens and hobs was a long, open-top saladette fridge, still containing the ingredients from the night before in the containers resting in the top of it. The police had obviously taken samples judging by the haphazard way everything had been left. She was half expecting Emily or Colin to walk back in at any moment and begin dinner service. They would only need to flip the gas back on and they could begin work immediately. There was even still a box of defrosted oven chips left by the dirty fryer; the grease had set hard around the top of it. Margery cringed; they would certainly have never planned to eat here if they had been able to see what a mess the place was.

'Do you know what that man ate, Margery?' Clementine asked her. She was peering into the top of the saladette with great interest, holding her phone upright to take photos. 'There's a weird bag of leaves here behind the fridge.'

Margery looked too but saw nothing of great interest. She was more concerned about where the kitchen paperwork was; there didn't seem to be any in the entire kitchen. Not a fridge temperature sheet or even a food probe to take temperatures with. It was possible that they used an all-in-one sheet book and the police had confiscated it, but surely there would be some remnants of food safety. There was not a pack of probe wipes in sight, not even a bottle of sanitiser or a health and safety poster. It was the opposite of her kitchen at work where the walls were drowning in laminated food legislation warnings and allergen information. Margery felt her thoughts go racing at a million miles an hour. If they had given a patron an allergic reaction knowingly then both Emily and Mr Warrell could be facing an enormous fine, but from what Detective Penfold had told them it had been deliberate. She would be interested to see whether they could provide the officers with up-to-date allergen paperwork, a spark of curiosity welling inside her. Maybe whoever had been cooking had known about Mr Jenkins's allergy and set up the entire thing deliberately.

The handwash sink on the wall didn't look as though it had been used for months, maybe even years. The only piece of paperwork she could see was the delivery document pinned to the board on one of the walls that read 'Broc 'n' Roll Greengrocer's'. She chuckled to herself at the pun.

'Clem, look at this.' Margery pointed at the document.

Clementine snapped a photo of it on her phone. She had been photographing the disgusting shelving units covered in a layer of dust and grease. 'We really should report this place to the local council and get environmental health to shut it down. I think you can do it online nowadays.'

There was a sudden noise from up the stairs and Margery and Clementine had only a moment to stare at each other in panic before Clementine grasped Margery by the wrist and dragged her out through the adjoining door into the restaurant and out behind the bar. You would never have known that anything had happened in the restaurant to look at it now. They stood for a second to catch their breath and before they could leave through the double doors across the room, the hinged kitchen door was swinging open once more, and they were face to face with a familiar young man with a pointed, beak-like nose.

'Thomas!' Margery cried. She briefly considered running and dragging Clementine with her, but it was much too late.

'Oh.' Thomas stopped what he was doing and stared at them, scratching his blonde head. He looked as though he had just got out of bed, which Margery supposed was quite plausible as it was still early, and he was wearing his pyjamas. 'Hello. What are you doing here?'

'We were just finding Clementine's handbag.' Margery said the first thing that arrived in her head and then regretted it immediately.

'Oh, right.' Thomas scratched his head again, looked even more confused than he had before. 'Well, let me know if you need any help.'

He picked up the broom in the corner as if that was what he had come into the room for.

'How's your dad?' Margery asked, though she didn't know why that question had come into her head either. They needed to leave before Thomas realised that Clementine was holding her handbag in her hand.

Thomas began to sweep the dirty floor with the brush. 'He's all right. A bit shaken and obviously the police have lots of questions. It's not every day something like that happens, is it? Poor Nathan.'

'Did you know him well?' Clementine asked curiously.

Thomas looked at her, a bit surprised, as if he wasn't expecting to be interviewed by them today. But he obliged her. 'Yeah, I did actually. Dad had some business planned with him. Such a shame none of it's going to happen now...' His voice puttered off and he looked away.

'Your father had plans to do business with the mayor?' Margery asked.

'Yeah.' Thomas nodded but did not elaborate.

'What happened to him?' Clementine asked; Margery could hear the nerves in her voice. Thomas shook his head. 'Was he allergic to something in the food? What did he have to eat?'

'Emily said he had the salmon and sorrel sauce. I don't know about any allergies, but the police haven't hung around so that's probably what it is,' he said, shifting from foot to foot, still holding the broom. 'You'll have to ask them when they finish their investigation, I suppose.'

'Of course,' Margery said. 'I suppose that's where Emily is, then?'

'Yeah, they were asking her all sorts about her gardening,' Thomas said. His voice had a casual air to it. It was almost breezy in its chill calmness. Margery found it a bit unsettling after what had happened to the mayor. She had forgotten that they had seen Emily gardening the day before outside the hotel.

'Does she do all the gardening here?' Clementine asked. 'Isn't George the gardener?'

'Some. George is the gardener, but she helps him,' Thomas said, in a way that told Margery that she probably did a great deal of the hotel's gardening.

'Have you not been asked anything by the police?' Clementine asked curiously.

'Yeah, but I couldn't really answer any of their questions.' Thomas smiled. 'It was my day off; I was playing on the PlayStation all night.'

'Oh,' Margery said. Thomas did not seem much like his father at all. Maybe he did all his shooting on the games console rather than in fields. He didn't really look much like his father either, though Colin was so much older than his son that it was hard to tell what features they may have shared in his youth. 'Who was the chef last night, do you know?'

Thomas gave her a look that told her he'd said too much. 'Look, I'd best get on. Dad'll go mad if he comes back and nothing's clean. I'll let you get off. Listen, dinner's off tonight. For obvious reasons, but I'll give you a discount on the room when you leave at the end of the week, okay?'

'Oh, we've already left the keys... We've decided not to stay. Given the circumstances.'

'Oh, right!' Thomas said. 'No worries, then. I'll sort you a discount in a bit when I've finished cleaning.'

They nodded weakly as he practically skipped from the room with the broom, whistling.

'He's a bit too happy, isn't he?' Clementine whispered.

'Yes,' Margery said, scratching her chin. The young man had certainly not seemed particularly worried about the events of the evening before, especially as the mayor had been an acquaintance of the family. They made their way through the dining room, out into the reception and finally around into the car park again. Margery looked over at the empty caravan and wondered again where George had gone.

Chapter Four

'I know it's a bit spooky because it's quiet...' Clementine said, looking around the deserted car park. 'But it's eerie out here, isn't it?'

'Yes,' Margery said. 'Where is everyone? Are they still in custody?'

'Well, Thomas is in there pottering about, isn't he?' Clementine pondered. 'I don't understand how he's allowed out and about.'

'What should we do?' Margery asked her.

'I vote we go and look at the caravan.' Clementine held her hands up. 'Seems as good a plan as any. See what George was hiding. He must have a reason to have run off; why are they looking for him otherwise?'

Margery turned to look where Clementine was pointing.

'You can't be serious?' she said. 'This is exactly what I'm worried about us getting dragged into!'

'We've got nothing to lose, have we?' Clementine began to march towards the caravan. Margery thought of the many things they could lose if they were caught at George's caravan, but she followed behind Clementine anyway.

They opened the gate to the field behind the hotel and walked briskly to the static caravan sitting inside it. It was an older model, four-berth at the very most, and George

45

had obviously lived there for quite some time judging by the tidy decorations on the outside and the careful paintwork that had been touched up. It was the type that you could pull with a car and people cursed at when stuck behind on a country road, but it had not been moved for years, judging by how rusted and weathered the tow bar looked. Margery almost felt bad for intruding on George's private space but needs must; there had been a death and they had to get to the bottom of it all, if only for their own peace of mind. The door was already open and still blowing in the breeze. Margery wondered if George had left it open on purpose or had forgotten to lock it during his quick exit. Perhaps the police had already been here looking for him and had left it unlocked. She stepped up into the tiny kitchen area and Clementine followed.

There was not much of note inside: a little kitchenette with a tiny fridge covered in magnets and postcards and a sink that still had a dish waiting to be washed in it. A main living area with two long sofas, a table and an even thinner door that opened into a cupboard-sized bathroom with barely room for the toilet and shower that were hidden inside. A single chest of drawers in the living room, with all the drawers pulled out of it and clothes falling all over the floor.

'Well,' Margery said. 'He's definitely not here.'

'No,' Clementine said, looking around the room with her hands on her hips. 'Shall we have a look and see if there's anything useful?'

Margery looked around the tiny caravan. There was not much to look at. An old battery-powered radio on the windowsill with an old coffee cup sitting next to it, the tricolour flag hanging on the left-hand wall above it. She went to the only thing of note in the room, a small bookcase, and began to rummage around though she wasn't sure what they were looking for. Most of the books were about gardening and she flipped through them. She picked up *The Big Book of British Plants* by Blodwyn E. Hammersmith and opened it to the first page. Instead of being greeted by a dry and dusty tome about boring flowers, she was met with a tiny scrawl of handwriting written in ballpoint pen. She almost dropped the book in surprise.

Went to the fair today, it rained the entire time!

She flipped through the next few pages; it was a diary. Though she was not sure what use it would be, as all the dates were from decades ago.

'Anything on the bookcase?' Clementine asked, flicking through the singular kitchen cupboard.

'George's diary, I think,' Margery said, showing the book to Clementine. 'But it's really old.' Clementine ran her hands through her hair in frustration.

'An old diary. Gosh, what a waste of time,' Clementine said. Margery put it into her handbag anyway.

'What about those on the fridge?' Margery pointed to the postcards held on with magnets. Clementine shook her head, lifting one off to show her.

'Nothing particularly interesting,' she said, turning it over in her hands to read the squiggly writing. 'Someone's having a great time in Greece, et cetera.'

Margery put her hands on her hips and looked around the tiny room again.

'Do you think those sofas turn into a bed?' Clementine asked her, placing her finger on her lips thoughtfully.

'Why?' Margery asked suspiciously. 'Don't tell me you want to get one?'

Clementine chuckled. 'We're quite co-dependent, but I think you'd kill me if we went away in one of these.' Margery laughed. 'No, I was just thinking that if I had something to hide, I'd put it somewhere that wasn't accessed easily.'

'Do you think he's left anything here?' Margery scratched her head. 'I'm beginning to think he took it all. Wouldn't the police have found anything useful?'

'He can't have carried everything,' Clementine reassured her. 'And they obviously haven't found anything either if they're asking us about it!'

They approached the sofas and table with the trepidation of a lion tamer approaching a wild beast. Margery had certainly never tried to put a caravan bed up or down. She didn't think Clementine ever had either. They stared at it for a moment. In the end, Clementine reached out tentatively and flipped the cushions from the sofa as though they would burn her if she touched them too long. Once they were gone, it became obvious that the seats were also storage cupboards.

'Bingo!' Clementine said. 'Let's have a look.'

She opened the first with a creak and they peered inside. There was nothing but neatly arranged piles of clothes, all winter jumpers and boots. They opened the other and were greeted by the same storage area.

'Hmmm,' Margery said, rubbing her chin. 'Gosh, I really thought you were on to something there.'

Unperturbed, Clementine began to rummage through the first drawer.

'There's got to be something here, Margery!' She continued to scrabble through his things and Margery took the initiative to do the same through the other drawer.

Clementine came up empty-handed, but Margery's fingers brushed something smooth and wooden. She dragged it out and gasped as she saw what it was. Clementine turned at the sound and stared at the photo frame too. It was three people standing outside The Boar's Head hotel's front entrance.

On the left was a much younger George, with his arms folded across his chest and beaming at the camera. He still had full, thick black hair and moustache. He was wearing a white chef's jacket and striped butcher's apron, and a traditional chef's toque. The woman to the right was wearing a T-shirt and apron and looked to also be part of the team. But Margery's eye was drawn to the woman standing between both of them; she did a double-take, feeling her mouth drop open. Wearing the exact same expression and exactly the same garb as George was a dark-haired woman the spitting image of Clementine.

'Is this you?' Margery asked Clementine, who scoffed.

'No!' Clementine said. 'Of course not. Well…I don't think so. I certainly haven't met George before. That doesn't look anything like me!'

'It does!' Margery stared at the photograph incredulously. Clementine huffed.

'My hair is much better than that, Margery!'

Margery opened the frame at the hinge and took the back off, revealing the same scrawl she had seen in the diary in her bag. *Chefs at the reopening of The Boar's Head hotel 1993!* it exclaimed excitedly.

'George must have been the chef on last night,' Clementine said. 'That must be why he's run.'

'And why they're looking for him,' Margery said. Clementine snapped a photograph on her phone, where it joined the others from the hotel, and then they hid it back under the clothes and folded the bed back together.

Nothing more to be found, they left the caravan and made their way back towards the car park. They had just made it to the fence at the edge of the field when Clementine grabbed Margery by the hand and pulled her down to hide behind the bushes lining the gate. She started to ask Clementine what on earth she was doing, but Clementine shushed her. They peered through the bars of the field's gate.

Detective Penfold and her deputy were helping Colin Warrell's fiancée climb out of the back of the police car. She looked ghastly, not a patch on the well-made-up young woman they had met only yesterday. There were huge bags under her red eyes. Margery wracked her brain for the woman's name but didn't need to as the back door to the hotel was flung open and Colin Warrell came storming out.

'Emily!' he cried. He was leaning on his walking stick but still making great strides towards Emily and the police officers. He did not look well either, though he hadn't the first few times they had met him. Today, though, he had a yellow undertone to his skin that made him look even more pallid and pasty than he had before. Rupert bounded out behind him, nearly tripping Colin as he rushed towards Emily.

'Finally brought her back, have you?' he yelled loud enough for Margery to hear metres away. Detective Penfold raised her eyebrows. Emily rushed to Colin and flung herself into his arms, nearly knocking him over. Rupert the dog bounced around them, barking. Colin glared at the police officers. If looks could kill, it would have melted the skin from Detective Penfold's face. She stared back at him, cold and unwavering. Had Mr Warrell been at the hotel the entire time they had been here? Margery wondered with cold horror.

'I told you she didn't do anything!' he continued to roar. 'I'm a respected businessman in this town. I own this hotel; does that count for nothing?'

Detective Penfold just stared at him coolly, as though he was a toddler throwing a tantrum.

Margery had found her intimidating earlier, but she was practically petrifying now. Mr Warrell pushed Emily off him; she continued to sob as he took a step towards Penfold. She did not even flinch.

'Oh, I see how it is,' he spat, his face reddening even more than Margery could ever have believed possible. 'You're all the same, can't let go of the past! You've had it out for me for years, Tanya. Leave Emily out of your stupid nonsense; it's got nothing to do with her – she's innocent. You come swanning back here from the city, with your stupid title. Piss off back to Plymouth, will you?'

They knew each other. And quite well if Colin knew Detective Penfold's first name, Margery thought. She wondered what had happened for them to share the animosity. From the disdainful look on Penfold's face, it was clear that she did not like Mr Warrell either.

'Colin!' Emily wailed from behind him, but he ignored her.

'A man died on your property, Mr Warrell. It's our job to question everyone involved,' Detective Penfold repeated, though his use of her forename had obviously rattled her. 'I'm beginning to wonder why you aren't more upset about that.'

'Obviously I'm upset,' he sneered. 'Nathan was a good friend of mine. How many times do I have to tell you? You need to go and find out where the hell George disappeared to; I bet you'd get some answers then! I gave you the kitchen rota. He was the chef on duty. You find him!'

'We are still searching for him,' Detective Penfold said wearily. 'And we will continue to look for him until we get him in custody, don't you worry about that.'

'You can't be looking very hard,' Colin snapped. 'How far away could he be? Honestly, you lot need to sort it out and you ought to be asking those women what the hell they're doing in the village!' he yelled. 'George was the chef on, I keep telling you!'

Margery was glad that neither he nor Detective Penfold had looked in their direction yet. Luckily, for the moment, Colin was so wrapped up in his own fury that he had not noticed the unfamiliar car in his own car park.

'They turn up out of the blue one minute and then the next a man's dead. And the face, that one woman's face, you know exactly who she looks like!'

Emily tried to drag him away but he pushed her off him and kept pointing at the police; she fell to the floor, still sobbing. 'You've got to find George; he'll know who she is. I'm sure of it. I should have asked her some questions myself when she was here. I bet they're all in it together.'

'Mr Warrell, you need to calm down and let us do our jobs,' Detective Penfold snapped at him. Colin threw his hands up in rage and stormed back into the building. Detective Penfold helped Emily up and disappeared into the building after him.

'Well, at least it's not only us that suspects George. If he was the chef on duty then no wonder they're interested in finding him,' Margery said.

'I wonder who Colin was talking about?' Clementine said. 'Was he talking about us?'

'I think…maybe?' Margery said, peering through the fence to make sure they were definitely gone. 'I can't see why, though. What could we have done?'

They stood and began to walk to the car at a fast pace, desperate to get away from the hotel again. Margery thought for a moment about the photograph at George's. Then, deciding nothing of it, she shook the thoughts away.

Chapter Five

They received a hero's welcome back at Rose's house. It was as though they never saw the rest of the dinner lady team at all, let alone every single day of term, which had only finished three weeks ago. They all looked ridiculously normal outside of their usual work clothes. Gloria was wearing her long black hair out of her usual neat plait for once; Margery marvelled at how long and pretty it was. Even Sharon and Karen had managed to not wear exactly the same outfit by mistake today. Usually they would turn up to places like an adult version of the twins from *The Shining*. Seren was still dressed like a beige cardigan that had come to life and escaped from the very back of the wardrobe, but Margery decided that it suited her. They nearly tripped over the mountain of bags piled up in the hallway as they made their way into the house.

'Hello, ladies!' Clementine beamed excitedly as they arrived in Rose's kitchen. It had seemed huge this morning but was now shrinking rapidly under the bags of shopping and wine, and numerous Summerview Secondary School staff, who were all gathered inside. 'What are you doing here?'

Rose looked particularly unimpressed as she held court at the head of the table. The Summerview school kitchen team had been invited to the party only begrudgingly, mostly because they were going to help Margery and

Clementine prepare all the food, and it was obvious she had not been expecting them so soon. She looked as though she had just drunk a big glass of curdled milk and then eaten an entire lemon.

Young Ceri-Ann turned from where she was trying to stuff another bottle of prosecco into the fridge and beamed back. The fridge door swung and narrowly missed hitting Seren in the face as Ceri-Ann rushed over to Margery and Clementine.

'We all came early after we heard what happened!' Ceri-Ann said loudly. The other dinner ladies in attendance nodded and there was much babbling about how Clementine and Margery had been arrested unfairly. They tried to explain, to little avail, that they had not actually been arrested, but were drowned out by the gaggle of voices.

'Couldn't let you solve this case all on your own, could we, girls?' Ceri-Ann shouted over everyone. There was an even bigger uproar at that, as they all agreed. 'And every time you try and fix something one of you nearly dies, don't ya? So, it's best we're all here to help.'

'We're not really trying to investigate, though, just clarify a few things,' Margery said, bewildered.

'You saw that kitchen, Margery,' Clementine said with an air of chaotic drama and a wave of her hand, as the others fell into an intrigued silence. '*Anything* could have happened in there.'

'Did you see the kitchen? Really!' Seren said excitedly. 'Did it have a salamander grill?'

'That poor man!' Sharon said as she burst into tears. Karen patted her on the shoulder comfortingly.

'There, there, Sharon,' she said. 'He's eating at God's restaurant now. Let's try not to let it ruin our holibobs.'

Clementine glared at them both, though Margery was certain that it was more for the abbreviation of 'holiday' than out of any sentiment for the mayor.

'So, what the hell happened here?' Ceri-Ann asked, pulling out a chair next to Margery. 'With the guy dying and that, not the hen party stuff. We don't care about that – I mean…' Rose glared at her from across the table. 'Well, it's better than my mate Chantelle's party already.' Ceri-Ann chuckled. 'We couldn't find anywhere that would rent a house for a hen, so we told them it was a mum retreat instead. But then they kept coming over and we had to keep hiding the balloons and willy straws.'

'There will be none of that!' Rose spluttered, almost spitting a mouthful of tea onto Seren.

Ceri-Ann shook her head sadly. 'They caught us in the end when we forgot to take the big hen party banner down from the living room and you could see it though the garden doors. Anyway, tell us, tell us! What happened?'

'Well!' Clementine sat down on her other side and gave a dramatic wave of her hand. 'What hasn't happened!'

The occupants of the room all fell silent, the sound of the kettle clicking off as it came to boil the only noise as they all leaned in to listen. Clementine gestured again as though she had a tremendous burden on her shoulders.

'As you know, I am fantastic at booking things on the internet…' Clementine began; Margery tried not to smile. 'So, we ended up at an absolutely fabulous hotel. A *boutique* hotel, much the sort of thing you'd find in Bath or Ittonvale or even…London.' Karen and Sharon gasped. 'Artesian water in the room, you know, assorted bath oils in the bathroom, an open-air ensuite…' The dinner ladies in attendance all 'oohed' at Clementine's vaguely descriptive lies about the dusty hotel room. Margery wondered what on earth an open-air ensuite even was. Clementine took a deep breath and continued. 'Well, anyway, we went for dinner there on our first evening and that's when he died – the mayor of the village.'

Clementine's bravado faded as she remembered what had happened. She looked away from the table, her shoulders drooping. Margery reached over and patted her on the hand gently.

'How did he die?' Ceri-Ann whispered.

'It was really awful. We thought he'd had an allergic reaction or something. His lips and tongue were all swollen, but the police seem to think he was murdered,' Margery said faintly, her own voice barely a whisper. She looked around the table at the other ladies gathered; they all had the same wide-eyed look. By retelling the tale out loud, Margery had again begun to wonder if the man's death had been as accidental as she had originally thought.

'He choked to death on his own tongue before the ambulance even got there,' Clementine said matter-of-factly, though Margery noticed her fingers playing with the paper napkin on the table in front of her. 'Just terrible. And the police asked us lots of strange questions! They're looking for one of the hotel workers and we think they think we were in cahoots with him, for some reason. They kept asking us where the hotel gardener has gone.' All the ladies gasped in outrage. Clementine continued, 'And then we went to the hotel and went into their disgusting kitchen, look!'

She picked up her phone, unlocked it and held it up so they could all see.

'Look, isn't that disgusting!' she said. 'You can see the fingerprints on the worktops!'

'That's a photo of you in a sunhat.' Seren pointed at the screen.

Clementine snatched the phone back and flipped through her photos to the one she wanted to show them, which was of the hotel kitchen's open-top saladette fridge. 'Look, look at that dirty fridge!'

Everyone leaned in expectantly.

'Can I see that?' Ceri-Ann asked. Clementine handed her the phone. 'What did you say the man ate?'

'Some kind of sorrel salmon dish, the owner's son told us,' Clementine said.

'Really? Huh.' Ceri-Ann raised her eyebrows.

'Why?'

'Because...' Ceri-Ann said thoughtfully, rubbing her chin as she looked closer at the picture. 'That looks like lords-and-ladies in there.'

'I can assure you that neither a lord nor a lady has ever stepped foot in that place,' Clementine said, taking a custard cream from the plate in the middle of the table. 'Apart from the lord mayor and it didn't end well for him, did it?'

'No, in the fridge. It's a plant that looks like sorrel.' Ceri-Ann shook her head, reaching over and zooming in on the photo with her fingers. 'That's not sorrel anyway, even if it's not lords-and-ladies.'

'What's the difference?' Margery asked. 'And how on earth do you know how to tell?'

'You know I love herbs and that, Margery!' Ceri-Ann said. 'You can pick some lush stuff just out in the woods. Me and my dad always go and forage for wild garlic and mint. I use them in my homemade body scrubs and aromatherapy oils. You've got to be careful, though, because you can pick some nasty stuff by mistake. Like

59

that.' She nodded at the phone before handing it back to Clementine.

'What's wrong with it?' Clementine demanded, staring at the photo again as if the mystery would reveal itself if she glared hard enough.

'Lords-and-ladies is really poisonous,' Ceri-Ann said. 'It can make you stop breathing and swell up. If it was lords-and-ladies in the sauce and not sorrel then that's probably what happened to your man. They're easily confused. I remember my dad and I found some giant hogweed once; we had to report it to the police because if you touch the leaves then they burn you really badly.'

'The police seemed to think it wasn't an accident,' Margery said, the realisation that they may have stumbled across the murder weapon dawning on her. Was a plant still considered a weapon?

She looked between them both, from Ceri-Ann's relaxed expression to Clementine still turning the phone around and around in her hands. Across from her, Rose's mouth was hanging wide open.

Rose made a strangled noise and leaped up from the table, her hands shooting up to cover her mouth. The cup of tea in front of her bounced and Seren jumped, causing her to drop her Bourbon biscuit on the floor. 'This can only mean one thing.' Rose's eyes were wide with horror. Margery had never seen her look like that ever in all the years they had known each other. 'The poisoner is back!'

–

The kitchen descended into complete chaos after Rose's bizarre interjection. Sharon had fainted, though Karen had caught her before she hit her head on the kitchen counter. Gloria had fanned her with a paper napkin till she came around again. After that, Margery gently suggested that they go outside and sit in Rose's designated smoking area in the garden, since the rain had stopped, and calm down, while Rose explained herself in the kitchen.

'Who the hell is the poisoner?' Clementine asked, brow furrowed.

'I was going to tell Margery about it earlier, before those dreadful police officers arrived and stole you,' Rose said dramatically. 'I don't remember much about it, because it all happened thirty-odd years ago. Too young, you see.' She flipped her perfect silver bob behind her ear smugly. 'But from what I remember...' Her voice dropped to a conspiratorial whisper, and they all leaned forward to listen. 'They were a person who poisoned people.'

'You're telling us some mad person was running about poisoning people?' Clementine said. 'And you never thought to mention it?'

Rose cut her off with her best deputy head glare. 'The locals were terrified. People couldn't drink a cup of tea or go to a pub without being afraid they were next!'

'What happened to them?' Margery asked. Clementine's eyes were wide next to her.

'Nobody knows.' Rose shrugged. 'They disappeared about thirty years ago and the poisonings stopped as soon as they did.'

'Is that it?' Clementine chastised. 'Well, how interesting and exciting. What a fascinating and useful piece of information you've given us.'

'Well, it's just a story now! A local legend,' Rose said, crossing her arms. 'Just something people bring up now and again in the pub, and I remember reading about it at the time. I was only twenty or so— no, I must have been twenty-three because I'd just finished my PGCE, and I'd applied to Summerview and Ittonvale but hadn't heard back from either yet.' Her eyes were glazed over as she stumbled through her memories. 'I was courting Christopher, one of the farmers' sons. It was before I met Barty, you see. Christopher's coming around for lunch tomorrow; we're still good friends. God, talk about a trip down memory lane...'

'So needless information about your love life aside,' Clementine said, 'what do you actually remember about the poisoner?'

'Not a lot unfortunately.' Rose looked almost apologetic. 'I'd forgotten all about it until last night. No one talks about it any more.'

They fell quiet. Margery looked around at the kitchen walls, which seemed cold and bare compared to their small house, which was drowning under the weight of all their sentimental items and furniture coated in cat hair.

'How was it not national news?' Gloria asked. 'I've certainly never heard anything about it, and I've been in the country more than thirty years.'

'Yeah, I'm Googling it and nothing's coming up.' Ceri-Ann held up her phone. 'Look, nothing, mate.'

'Well, I don't say what gets on the news, do I?' Rose said, throwing her hands up. 'Anyway, you've been here a few days. Surely you've realised how private this area is.'

Margery nodded. St Martin's was quite affluent from what she had seen driving past the houses with private driveways and gates. It made sense that people would keep to themselves.

'Do you know him, Rose? The man who died?' Margery asked the woman sitting opposite her. 'Nathan Jenkins?'

'Not really,' she said, scratching her head, her brow furrowed as she thought about it. 'I know of him. He owns the golf club and a few other places, I think, and like I said, he was on the town council. You couldn't miss him with all the gold chains on, jingling about the place all the time.'

'You can't think of a reason anyone would kill him?' Clementine asked her.

'Well, no.' Rose shook her head. 'But I don't really know him personally. There is one thing I thought of this morning, but I'm afraid I don't know too much about it. I'm only here for a few weeks a summer.'

'What is it?' Margery asked.

'Colin Warrell ran against Nathan Jenkins for mayor and lost to him,' Rose said. 'It was a few years ago now, though.'

'Really?' Margery and Clementine said in unison.

'Well, that would explain him having a grudge, wouldn't it?' Gloria said triumphantly.

'But his son said they had some sort of business together so they must have been on all right terms,' Margery said. Clementine stroked her chin, deep in thought. 'You don't go into business with someone you hate, do you? And you don't just kill your business partner.'

'You'd be better talking to some of Nathan's friends or family, wouldn't you?' Rose asked.

'His wife,' Margery said to Clementine. Clementine nodded.

'Yes, his wife will know about Colin Warrell losing out on mayor; she might know more about this poisoner too if she's lived here a long time. But where else can we find out anything about it if there's nothing online?' Clementine said. She had taken Ceri-Ann's phone from her and was scrolling through aimlessly while Ceri-Ann tried to snatch it back.

'I don't know,' Rose said. 'Maybe the local paper? They'd probably be quite interested, probably know more about him and why anyone would want to kill him. Hang on, I think I have a copy somewhere.' She jumped up and walked out into the hall. They could hear her rummaging around in the drawers of the Welsh dresser. 'I usually just put it straight in the recycling after reading,' she called out. 'Here it is!'

She arrived back in the kitchen and put the paper down on the table in front of Margery and Clementine with a thump. 'Don't know why I pay for it to be delivered, to be honest – it's mostly car adverts and things about children I don't care about.'

Margery picked up the latest edition of the *St Martin's Chronicle* and peered at the cover. There was nothing particularly exciting there. The local school was having a book fayre next week and the now-deceased mayor was supposed to be opening the new, and long-awaited, electric car charging station in the supermarket car park at the top of town. A Range Rover driver was complaining about the new electric charging station in the supermarket car park at the top of town. It was all very dreary.

'The police didn't seem that interested in Colin, though,' Margery said as she flipped through the pages. There was obviously nothing about the mayor dying or anything else of that kind; this issue was too old. 'They took his fiancée off to interview her, but he was already back at the hotel.'

'Hmmm.' Rose stroked her own chin. 'That's interesting. I don't know much about her, to be honest.'

'Do you know much about anyone?' Clementine asked. 'Apart from your exes?'

Rose ignored her outburst and continued, 'I think a lot of the locals see her as a bit of a gold digger. That's what I've heard down the pub, anyway. She's certainly not with him for his looks. She's almost the same age as his son; maybe the police think she had something to do with it all because of that?'

It made a certain amount of sense, Margery thought as she skimmed an article about the mayor's upcoming summer fete plans.

'Let's get down to the newspaper office; that's our best hope, isn't it?' Clementine said. 'Where's the address?'

Margery found it on the 'letters to the editor' page, next to a demand for the village teenagers to be banned from the local post office by a Mrs Petunia Wainwright.

'You're not thinking of going down there?' Gloria said. 'Surely you can't go getting involved in all of this?'

'Yeah, the police are already being weird with you, aren't they?' Ceri-Ann said. 'Maybe one of us should go instead.'

'Maybe,' Margery said but Clementine interrupted.

'No, we have to go,' she said, pointing to the address on the newspaper. 'We're the dinner lady detectives, aren't we? It's not "the dinner lady detectives and friends", is it?'

'Well, maybe it should be,' Rose said. 'Then you wouldn't have had so much trouble at Christmas with that dog-napping, would you? Let them help; it'll get them out of my house for a bit.'

'Yeah, and this is literally what we came here for, mate,' Ceri-Ann said, taking a cigarette out of the pack in her pocket and passing another to Rose. Rose opened her mouth to speak but Ceri-Ann interrupted her. 'Yeah, smoking outside, I know, I know, don't worry!' Rose harrumphed. Ceri-Ann continued, 'Anyway, it'll get a bit boring here if we don't get to do the murder bit too. Might as well've stayed at Butlin's and done the bingo and murder mystery night.'

Margery shook her head. 'Do you think all of us going down there would be okay? I think they're more likely to speak to Clem and I alone.'

Clementine nodded. Ceri-Ann held her hands up in surrender and got up to go into the garden. Gloria shook her head and tutted. Rose looked like she wanted to say something, but no one said another word.

Chapter Six

The newspaper offices did not take a long time to find. They were operating on the first floor of the village library, a tiny building attached to the pay and display car park at the edge of St Martin's-on-the-Water. The village centre, if you could call it that, was miniscule compared to the long high street they usually wandered up and down at home. It was set more in a square than anything else, and she could see the post office, which seemed to also be operating as a convenience store, and the little gift shop from the car park. There was a thatched-roof pub in the other corner, a village hall, which a group of elderly people were playing bowls outside of, and not much else. The high street ran downwards and they could see row upon row of quaint little houses at the bottom leading towards the end of the village. It was a strange little place, most of it being built on the cliffs. Even on a bad weather day you could see over across the water to the beach and Merrowpool. Margery still hoped they might get a chance to drive across and visit the town at some point; a day on the beach would raise the spirits, if nothing else. They had booked the hotel on the basis of the cliff path that led through the fields at the back of the car park and straight down. You could supposedly wander a lovely five-mile route across them to the beach on the neighbouring banks that she could almost see from the library car park, though she felt privately that they would almost certainly try out the local public transport network rather than undertake the walk.

Margery gathered her thoughts in the peace and quiet of the car as Clementine went over to the machine to pay for their parking ticket. She felt very on edge, and it was hard to steel her nerves enough to exit the car and go and face a group of strangers, who may or may not know what was going on. She assumed that they did; everyone else in town seemed to. Well, the hotel staff at least.

She wondered why they kept letting themselves get wrapped up in these things. Really, all she wanted to do was get through the next two or three years at work at a lovely easy pace, then retire and spend her time pottering in the garden or crocheting. It did not seem likely at this point, though Clementine had promised they would set a retirement date soon. They had both been eligible to take their private council pensions for a good few years now, lucky enough to be some of the few school kitchen workers in the country that had not been taken over by a larger outside catering company, and they had paid the house off long ago. They should be able to enjoy themselves comfortably until they were state pension age, as long as they were careful, but they were not extravagant people. This holiday had been the first proper trip away they had taken that was not school-related for years. Usually, they spent their summer holidays going on short walks in the countryside surrounding Dewstow or enjoying an afternoon in the park. To spend a holiday away was alien to her.

Clementine returned, opening the driver's side door and handing her the slip of paper. 'Right, we've got till two. I wanted to put in longer, but I only had two ten p's left.' She paused, seeing the look on Margery's face. 'Are you all right, sweetheart?'

'Yes, fine,' Margery said. She put the piece of paper on the windshield and clambered out of the car.

'We need to work on what we're going to say,' Clementine rambled as they headed into the library building. 'Or they'll just think we're crazy and kick us out.'

They needn't have worried. The library staff were so polite, they felt like guests of honour at a private party. A lady in a themed jumper featuring the works of Jane Austen pointed them up the stairs in the direction of the newspaper office and they blundered along the long, looming hallway, looking for the right number.

'Margery!' Clementine grabbed her by the wrist suddenly. She was pointing dramatically at a plaque on one of the office doors that simply read 'Mayor Jenkins'.

Before Margery could even say anything in reply, Clementine had let go of her wrist and reached out to try the door handle. With a *clack*, the door swung open gently, revealing a woman standing behind the desk. Margery could tell from her sore red eyes that she had been crying.

'Oh,' she said, wiping her face with a tissue, 'can I help you?'

'You're Nathan Jenkins's wife,' Clementine said in surprise. 'Gosh, I'm so sorry.'

'We were on our way to the newspaper office and got lost; all these council buildings look the same to us,' Margery tried to explain. Andrea Jenkins looked to be around their age, Margery thought, though she was much better put together than either she or Clementine. Her mid-length, curly dark hair was pinned back neatly, and she was wearing a sleeveless blouse and light blue capri trousers. She appeared much too wrapped up in her own grief to wonder how they had got the room number so spectacularly wrong, and she did not question them. Instead, she slumped down in Nathan's office chair.

'You were there the evening Nathan died,' she said softly. Her voice had a lilt to it; Margery could not place the location, though she felt it was probably Welsh. 'I remember you.'

'Yes.' Margery nodded, looking at Andrea's drawn face. The bags under her eyes seemed to be sinking into her skull, such was the depth of her exhaustion. 'We're very sorry about your husband, Mrs Jenkins.'

'Thank you,' she said, worrying the brim of the hat with her fingers. 'It's been awful.'

'I'm sure,' Clementine said. 'I can't imagine anything worse.' She gave Margery a quick look before turning back to Andrea.

'Sorry, I shouldn't be here. I've just come to start sorting his things.' She began to sob. Margery stepped forward and handed her the tissues from the desk. 'Thanks, it's just…the police haven't released his body yet and I don't know what to do with myself at home. They keep asking me stupid questions: do I know anyone who would kill him… Of course not; everyone liked my Nathan. He was very sociable; it's what made him good at his old business.'

'His job? You mean apart from being the mayor?' Margery asked softly.

'He owned…' Andrea stumbled on the words and took a deep breath before continuing. 'He owned an estate agency before he became mayor. He was always so busy after he took the job with town planning meetings and functions, but he tried to keep a foot in the door with it.'

She took another deep breath as though trying to calm herself. 'He had a lot of dealings with many people, but I can't think of a single enemy he would have had.'

'Do you know if there was anyone in particular that Mr Jenkins was doing business with at the time, Mrs Jenkins? Before he passed, I mean,' Margery asked, though they knew the answer from their talk with Thomas.

Andrea wiped her face as she thought about it. 'Well, of course. He was working with Colin Warrell; that's why we were at the hotel that evening. They had some big plan, finalising a deal after dinner.'

'Was that why you were both at the hotel?' Margery asked, thinking of the mayor's face that night.

'Yes,' Andrea said. 'Colin invited us over but he couldn't make it down to eat because he had too much to do, or so he said, though he managed to join us for a drink.' She shook her head and rolled her eyes in a way that told Margery exactly what she thought of Colin Warrell before remembering her audience. 'Anyway, Dr Bell joined us instead; well, you know the rest…'

They did, Margery thought darkly, all too well. 'Were Nathan and Colin good friends? Even after Colin ran against him for mayor?'

'Of course they were,' Andrea snapped. She stared between them both and didn't say anything more. Margery didn't know how to ask her. Maybe they were being too invasive; this poor woman's husband had just died. Margery knew that if Clementine had died, she would be beside herself with grief. 'They went hunting together all the time, best of friends. Who are you to come into his office and begin insinuating things?'

'I'm sorry,' Margery said, 'I just thought…'

'Well, don't.' Andrea glared at them both. 'Please leave.'

'We're sorry for your loss,' Margery said finally. Andrea slumped back in Nathan's chair.

—

They had comforted her as best they could and left her in peace, continuing their journey down the long hallway into a tiny office. The elderly lady behind one of two desks gave a start as they entered.

'Good Lord!' she cried, holding her hand to her heart. 'For a minute there I thought you were…but you can't be…' She shook her hands in front of herself as though shaking away a memory and stood from the chair. 'Sorry.' She held out her hand to shake Margery's. 'I'm Petunia Wainwright, lead reporter and editor. This is Sophie, part-time journalist, head tea maker.' She gestured to the other desk right at the back of the room and Margery realised with a start that there was another, much younger woman sitting there. The piles of papers and books had been so jarring at first that she had not noticed the small woman in the beige cardigan and thick glasses, perched behind the large, boxy computer. She waved over at them. Petunia Wainwright continued, 'Can I help you?'

Margery eyed the woman carefully and then looked at her wife. Petunia Wainwright was not the first person who had taken a gasp after seeing Clementine. Who on earth did they all think she was? Not a celebrity of some sort? Maybe there was a champion darts player who looked like her.

'We're certainly hoping you can,' Clementine said; she was looking around the tiny room. It was stuffed to the brim with stacks of old newspapers. Sophie's fingers clacked slowly as she used one finger to type at the ancient computer keyboard. Margery wondered how they ever got anything done in here. She could feel her breathing quicken as claustrophobia took hold in the tiny room. 'We were hoping you could help us with something that happened a long time ago.'

'I can certainly try,' Petunia said, gesturing for them to sit down on the tucked-in chairs in front of her desk. She sat back down too as they squeezed themselves down into the seats. 'What seems to be the problem? Parking fine? Missing fishing permit for the lake?'

Now that they were here and had a new person to tell their problem to, Margery felt that the whole thing was madness again. She reluctantly cleared her throat to begin to tell the tale.

'Have you heard what happened at The Boar's Head hotel, Mrs Wainwright?' she asked. Petunia Wainwright stiffened as though Margery had asked her where she might be able to purchase a large jar of slugs. Margery saw her eyes dart over Clementine's face curiously again, but then she looked back to Margery.

'I have,' she said finally. Her mouth was so puckered it was as though she had tried to drink an entire pint of lemon juice before they had arrived. She busied herself with the papers on her desk, though Margery could see that all her shuffling was just making more of a mess. Sophie had stopped typing and was now peering around from behind the computer and squinting at them in interest.

'Who are you?' Petunia glared at them both in suspicion.

'We're the dinner lady detectives,' Clementine said before Margery could stop her. 'We're very famous in Dewstow, and also Ittonvale.'

'I've never heard of either of those places,' Petunia said.

'The inventor of self-raising flour died in a nearby town,' Clementine said sincerely, as if that was explanation enough.

'So,' Margery said, cutting Clementine off. Petunia's mad filing had still not stopped. 'We've heard from a…er…well…a source, I suppose, that maybe this has something to do with the…ah…the…' She struggled to say the word out loud for fear of spooking the woman sitting in front of her, but Clementine did not have any such issues.

'The poisoner!' Clementine said. The woman almost jumped out of her seat, her hand leaping to her mouth as she gasped. She stared at Clementine again, in even more interest than before.

'How do you know about that?' she whispered. Her eyes bored into Clementine's. Margery watched the scene in suspense as chills began to run up her spine. 'Unless…? No, you can't be. They've gone.'

'Who's gone?' Margery asked in confusion. 'The poisoner?'

Petunia whipped around as though she had forgotten that Margery existed. Sophie ducked back behind the computer and began madly typing what was obviously nonsense in earnest.

'I've said too much,' Petunia said, standing from the desk and beginning to wring her hands as though she were wringing water from a damp tea towel. 'You've got to go.'

'No.' Clementine looked around the tiny office. 'Why should we?'

'The poisoner is gone?' Margery demanded. 'Is that what you mean? Where did they go?'

'I can't tell you anything, please stop asking,' Petunia spluttered.

'But...'

'No buts about it!' Petunia sat back down in her chair and gave Margery a pleading look. 'Please.'

'What about Nathan Jenkins?' Margery pleaded. 'Do you know anything about him?'

'Do I know anything about the mayor? Of course I do, and I'm not telling you a thing.' Petunia got up again.

'Why not?' Clementine asked as she shooed them from the room.

'Because I don't know you.' Petunia glared at her and then at Clementine. 'I especially can't talk to you!'

'Me?' Clementine pointed to her own face dramatically. 'Why especially me?'

Petunia realised that she had said too much and just glared at them both again, even more venomously than before.

She began her advance again and they found themselves being ushered back out into the library. They stood for a moment in defeat and shock. Margery could not quite believe that any of that had just happened. Why would Petunia not talk to them, about any of it? And why had the paper not reported on the story? The mayor of the village had died; surely that was breaking news, worthy of replacing the summer fete news on the front page. What on earth was Petunia Wainwright playing at?

'Well,' Clementine said as they began to make their way back into the car park. 'What a bust.'

'I know.' Margery sighed, taking Clementine by the arm. 'You've got to stop telling people we're detectives. It's never anything but trouble.'

'I bet Sherlock Holmes never had a problem telling people he was a detective,' Clementine said as they walked to the car arm in arm. 'I bet he used to tell everyone.'

'I don't think he did...' Margery said, 'as he was fictional.'

'That's what they want you to think, Margery!' Clementine began but she was interrupted by a cry from across the car park.

'Wait!' came a shout and they turned. 'Detectives!'

It was Sophie. She was running towards them through the car park, her long skirt and cardigan whipping behind her, her curly brown hair falling out of her short ponytail. She had taken her glasses off and was holding them as she sprinted, the lenses as thick as the bottom of a milk bottle. Margery could see as she reached them that she was even younger than she had thought when she had seen her behind the desk. She could barely have been school-leaving age; she didn't look much different to the top-form class students she saw daily at Summerview Secondary.

'Detectives!' she panted as she came to a halt in front of them and bent to catch her breath, resting her hands on her bare knees for a second. 'Detectives!'

'Are you all right?' Margery asked, bending down to look at the girl in concern. Sophie nodded at her. She stood finally and took a photo with the camera hanging around her neck on the lanyard so quickly that neither Margery nor Clementine had time to react before the flash was blinding them both. Margery had not even seen her wearing it before.

'What on earth!' Margery protested.

'You can't take a photo of—' Clementine began, but Sophie interrupted.

'Mrs Wainwright told me I had to! But look, I— I want to help you,' she stammered breathlessly. 'But Mrs Wainwright can't find out. She's going to report about Mr Jenkins's death; we've been planning it all day. But I need to warn you that you may not like it once it gets out.'

'Why not?' Clementine asked. 'What on earth is going on here!'

Sophie was bent double again, wheezing; they waited for her to recover. She finally gave one last cough and then stood again. Margery wondered whether she could step forward and grab the camera from her without much of a fight, but eventually thought better of it.

'Meet me back here tomorrow morning; I'll see what I can find tonight when she's gone home. I'll wait for you by the public toilet block over there.' Sophie pointed to the small stone building across the car park. 'Nine o'clock, okay?'

'Why would you do that?' Margery asked. 'Mrs Wainwright doesn't seem to want to help at all.'

'Colin Warrell is my grandmother's landlord!' Sophie said, as if that explained everything. 'Got to go, Mrs Wainwright will wonder why I'm taking so long to use the loo!'

She rushed back across the car park. Margery and Clementine watched her go in stunned silence.

Chapter Seven

'Do you know what I think we should do?' Clementine asked Margery as they clambered back into the car, still reeling from Sophie's sudden arrival.

'Go and get an afternoon tea?' she said, turning the key in the car ignition. The engine roared to life.

'Well, yes. The answer to that is always yes, you know that, but also…' Clementine lowered her voice as though she were worried about being overheard. 'We know the name of the company who supplied that plant, don't we?'

'Do we?' Margery said thoughtfully, pulling the car out of the parking space and beginning the journey back to Rose's house. She had a vague recognition of a name in her memory but couldn't quite put her finger on it.

'We do,' Clementine said smugly. 'I took a photo of the delivery document, didn't I? Broc 'n' Roll Greengrocer's – what a ridiculous name.'

'It is a bit ridiculous.' Margery thought about it as she drove carefully out of the car park and out onto the main road, which was no more than a country lane. Possibly it would be a good place to start, and they needed all the help they could get in case Sophie came up short. 'Sophie said that Mr Warrell was her grandmother's land-lord, didn't she? I wonder what she meant by that.'

'Well, that's not a bad thing to know either, is it?' Clementine said. 'If we don't get anything from the greengrocer, we can go to the estate agent's. I bet if Colin's a landlord they'd know him and they'd definitely know Nathan if he was an estate agent; I'll give them a Google. Ooh, it'll be a real tourist trip!'

'I think most tourists just go and sit on the beach in Merrowpool, Clem.' Margery chuckled. 'Well, where is this greengrocer's, then? Is it nearby?'

Clementine, who had been scrolling through her phone, shook her head. 'It is but it's closed already. Ridiculous. No wonder everyone gets everything from supermarkets now. We'll have to go first thing before we meet that strange woman again.'

'Sophie?' Margery said as the car puttered along. The scenery outside was green and pleasant now that the rain had finally died off. 'She didn't seem that strange.'

'She ran across a car park, Margery!' Clementine scoffed. 'And she wasn't even being chased.'

'And she did take a photo of us,' Margery agreed. 'God, what's happening here? Surely this isn't normal.'

They arrived back to Rose's house safely, trundling up the long entrance path and pulling into the gravelled driveway in front of the farmhouse. Karen and Sharon were still sitting outside on the immaculate front lawn drinking what were unmistakeably glasses of Pimm's from the jug on the table next to where they lounged on deckchairs. They had been joined by Gloria and Ceri-Ann, who were both sitting on the bench against the wall of the house. Seren was struggling along with a very old-looking push lawnmower around them, perspiring with the great effort it took to move it. As they stepped from the car, Rose came out of the house, wearing huge sunglasses and a floaty summer dress. She was carrying a picnic blanket and a full martini glass and was obviously headed for the garden too. A man in tweed trousers and a white shirt with the sleeves rolled up was following her, and he seemed to know the layout well, stepping off the concrete step without looking and smiling over at them. He looked around Rose's age, and just as well presented as she was. His dark hair and beard were neat and tidy; his sunglasses and the smart-looking boots with the stripe of neon yellow down the side were both obviously designer.

'How did you get on?' Rose called as they clambered out of the car. 'Come and sit down and tell us about it. Seren, you've missed a bit! By the greenhouse!'

'Don't worry, I'll finish that for you, Seren, give it here,' the man said, smiling at her and moving to take over the mowing. Seren beamed back.

'This is the Christopher I was telling you about.' Rose smiled too, gesturing to him before she arranged herself neatly into the deckchair. Seren flopped down on the grass next to her. Christopher pulled the pair of headphones he had around his neck over his ears and then began to push the lawnmower with the greatest of ease. He was quite handsome, Margery noted. She could imagine why Rose would have been enamoured with him as a teenager, his rugged facial features and slicked-back hair reminded her of the headmaster, though he was a lot younger. Rose obviously had a type.

Margery and Clementine waved hello to him and then joined the others on the lawn. They quickly explained what had happened while everyone listened. When they had finished telling the story, Ceri-Ann shook her head.

'That newspaper lady obviously knows something, then, don't she?' Ceri-Ann said. Margery nodded in agreement.

'She definitely does,' Margery said. 'I just wish we knew what.'

After a short internet search assisted by Ceri-Ann, they soon realised that both St Martin's-on-the-Water's little high street and Merrowpool's were made up almost entirely of estate agencies. All of them rented properties in some form or another. There was no way to tell which one Colin Warrell let his houses through.

'Someone will know something!' Clementine had said dramatically, but Margery reminded her that if they could not even manage to get the local reporter to spill the beans on Mr Warrell then they would never manage to get anything from a business he worked with. Especially as they were only assuming he even worked with a letting agency in the first place. For all they knew, he privately rented out a single house. It all seemed a bit of a dead end.

'Colin Warrell had business with the mayor, Thomas told us and Andrea confirmed it,' Margery mused as they lounged on the grass. She was glad that she had put on a layer of sun cream before they left the house that morning and forced Clementine to do the same, else they would have both been crispy by now. As it was, Karen and Sharon both had red strips on their legs where their shorts ended, and Ceri-Ann's nose was looking a bit redder than usual.

'Did he?' Ceri-Ann asked. 'Did he say what?'

'No, but it must be something to do with houses. The mayor used to be an estate agent.' Clementine sighed. 'I wish everyone would stop being so cryptic about everything, though, and spit it all out. That newspaper lady ought to have her newspapering licence taken off her.'

'Ooh, I agree!' Ceri-Ann said, picking another daisy from the lawn and adding it carefully to the pile in front of her crossed legs. 'Imagine the actual literal mayor dying and not even reporting on it. I've been looking online all day, mate, and there's been nothing about it at all. Ooh, though I did find out something that you might be interested in.'

'What?' Margery asked.

Ceri-Ann didn't answer; instead, she swiped through her phone and then handed it to Margery.

'Gosh,' Margery said, reading the Facebook post quickly. 'What's this from?'

'Merrowpool community Facebook page.' Ceri-Ann pointed to the screen. 'That's his wife, isn't it?'

'Yes.' Margery scrolled though the post again, looking at the comments. It was dated a few weeks ago and Andrea was asking for the return of her husband's gun, which had been stolen from their garage. There were several accompanying photographs of both him and the gun, a close-up showing an unusual engraving of a seagull on the butt of the weapon.

'She didn't mention that, did she?' Clementine said, reading the screen over Margery's shoulder.

'Well, of course she didn't.' Margery gave the phone back to Ceri-Ann. 'Why would she? She was right, we aren't real detectives. Anyway, they might have found the gun by now.'

'You're both my favourite detectives, though.' Ceri-Ann smiled at them. Margery smiled back weakly.

'If we're going to find out anything, then we're going to have to do it ourselves, I think,' Margery said. 'I've got a feeling anyone else we speak to here will close rank like Petunia and Andrea. They don't want two strangers poking around in village business, do they?'

'No. But we wouldn't in Dewstow either, would we?' Clementine picked at the grass with her fingertips, deep in thought, braiding it with her hands. 'I wonder where George from the hotel went.'

'Me too,' Margery agreed. Clementine gazed up at her from where she was lying back. 'A shame he didn't really leave any clues, and who better than to know what plants were poisonous than a gardener?'

Clementine shook her head. 'I can't believe he'd leave a kitchen like that. It was horrible in there, and he calls himself a chef?'

'It certainly didn't look like a chef had ever seen that kitchen,' Margery said, remembering the grease running out of the extraction above the hob. 'Not a professional one, anyway; even Ben wouldn't have left the place in such a state.'

Ceri-Ann and Clementine both smiled at the memory of their failed dinner person, Benjamin, who had been removed from the kitchen after one too many accidents involving shortcrust pastry.

'What about that book you took?' Clementine stroked her chin. 'With the diary in it – do you think that would be any use?'

'Maybe,' Margery said, but she was unconvinced. She reached over to where she had plopped her bag down in the grass and took the book out.

'*The Big Book of British Plants* by Blodwyn E. Hammersmith. I've read this one,' Ceri-Ann said, studying the book over her shoulder with interest. 'It's a bit boring. She's not the most exciting author, old Blodders.'

Margery turned to a random page and held it up so Ceri-Ann could see the writing inside. 'What's this, mate?'

84

'It's George's diary,' Clementine said. 'Margery stole it.'

'We both stole it,' Margery reminded her.

'Anything good in there?' Ceri-Ann asked.

'I don't know, really.' Margery flipped through it again, the tiny writing giving her a headache just from the sight of it. She decided she would try and read it all over the next few days, just in case there was something more to it. Otherwise they had stolen someone's private belonging from their home for no reason and she was beginning to feel very uneasy about it.

'What I don't get is why they questioned Emily as well,' Ceri-Ann said, 'if that George bloke was cooking and they're so sure it was him?'

Margery thought about that for the rest of the day, ruining what should have been a beautiful, relaxing afternoon in the sunshine that had been threatening to reappear for days and had arrived suddenly in all its glory. She was still thinking about it when they went to bed that evening. She set their alarm clock for an ungodly hour for a summer holiday, ready to visit the greengrocer before they saw Sophie again, but found herself drawn to George's diary. While Clementine snored, she opened the book again. The low light of the bedside table bathing the room in an orange glow was just light enough to read by.

She hadn't thought the contents would be that interesting, or helpful given how old it was, but it was October at the beginning of the diary and Mr Warrell – as the diary called him – was running shooting trips from the hotel.

George went into great detail about how to hang the pheasants the tourists killed and how they were preparing them in the hotel kitchen, what dishes they were coming up with. It was as much of a cookbook as a private diary, Margery thought as she read George's rambles about if dry or wet plucking was best. It was a treasure trove of useful culinary information, full of great methods. Like how if you were in a great rush and only wanted the breast meat from the game, you didn't need to pluck the whole bird; you could just make a little nick at the bottom of the bird's stomach with your sharpest knife and then rip all the feathers up in one go to reveal the meat underneath them, which you could then cut away as though it were simply a chicken you had bought from a supermarket. You could then pané and deep fry it to go with whatever you had managed to forage on the cliffs that day, all in time for dinner service at the hotel.

Margery could tell by the tone of the writing, though she wasn't sure entirely how, that the writer of the diary found the process slightly grotesque. There was a two-page-long entry dated 12th October 1993 that complained about a bird who had been shot by an eager patron through the stomach lining, and the smell that had filled the kitchen after they had gone to prepare it. George spent the entirety of the autumn and winter entries wishing it was spring or summer so he could find some more interesting things to cook with, that hadn't had to be shot to be eaten: rock samphire, wild strawberries, chickweed.

He often complained about a person he simply referred to as Fossil, his second-in-command, who he found very annoying and always under his feet. Margery wondered if one of the women in the photograph they had found was Fossil, though George was very careful not to gender anyone. Fossil seemed to be called so because of their age, so Margery suspected she must be the older woman in the photograph.

He complained about the rest of the hotel staff just as eagerly. There seemed to be a large rotating cast of them, all called silly things that couldn't possibly be their real names: Joplin, Scrubs, Bubbles. Maybe he was worried the diary would be found one day – his fears realised by Margery's reading, she thought – or perhaps these were what they called each other. Margery has certainly worked in kitchens that would use nicknames when she was younger.

The only person who escaped this treatment was Mr Warrell, who was referred to by his name, and whom George seemed to like and respect very much.

2nd December 1993

I was hoping my elderflower wine from the summer would be ready and IT IS, DIARY! Celebrating with a glass of it as we speak! Next year I'm going to make a dandelion one when they all pop up in the summer, better than having them all over the lawn. Fossil says I'll go blind if I do it wrong but what the hell do they know? Put a lovely special on tonight. I went to Merrowpool at the crack of dawn and found some winkles – I cooked them in salted water and then served them with some crusty bread and lots of salted butter. Delicious! Mr Warrell said it was the best yet, he's lovely, I think I'll take him down a glass of the wine to thank him for his kind words…

Margery put the diary down and rubbed her eyes, thoroughly exhausted. George knew as much about plants as they had suspected judging by the diary, but she was too tired to read on. It would have to wait until tomorrow when she would have a moment to pick it back up again without falling asleep.

Margery woke with a start. She lay still for a moment, wondering why on earth she was not still asleep before she heard it. Down on the ground floor, the doorbell was ringing – one long, continuous ring. Next to her, Clementine groaned and rolled over, pulling the duvet over her head as she did so.

Margery sat up and wiped sleep from her eyes; the clock across from them on the dressing table said that it was half past one in the morning. The doorbell stopped for a moment and she began to breathe a sigh of relief, but before she could even exhale all the air, it began again. Who could be calling at this hour? Margery was often wary of answering the door at very normal times of the day; a visitor in the middle of the night could never be a good thing. She wondered why no one else seemed to be answering it either. Surely if it was a planned visit, then whoever they were visiting would have been waiting near the door to let them in? Seren and Ceri-Ann had disappeared to the local pub hours ago. Perhaps they had forgotten their key and were trapped outside in the chill of the late summer morning.

Margery groaned and dragged herself out of bed. She tried to look out of the window to see if she could see the front doorway below, but it was much too high for her to peer down out of it. She pulled her dressing gown from the back of the guest room door and crept out into the hallway, leaving Clementine snoring. The long hall was empty and dark, and she rushed along it as the doorbell began to ring again, feeling her way along the walls. The closer she got to the stairs, the louder it seemed to ring. She made her way down the staircase, where she could see there was a single light glowing from the lamp on the sideboard table. The sound reverberated off the old farmhouse walls. Her feet were cool on the flagstone floors as she tiptoed towards the door, placing her hand on the handle.

She almost screamed when the hand touched her arm, jumping back into the hallway. She looked up to find Rose's pale face staring at her, her eyes wide in the dim light.

'Don't,' she hissed. 'I don't know who it is, and I'm not opening the door to a stranger in the middle of the night. My house is in the middle of nowhere; who would be calling? We're all here! Do you want to end up on a true-crime Netflix special?'

'But what if it's Ceri-Ann and Seren?' Margery whispered back. 'Didn't they go to the pub? Did they take a key?'

'I let those drunkards in hours ago.' Rose looked frightened now. She covered her ears as the doorbell rang again. 'I'm surprised they're not down here complaining about the noise.'

'So, what do we do?' Margery asked. The bell clanged again, and they stared at each other, wide-eyed. 'I don't think they're going to go away. Should we ring the police? I have that police officer's number.'

Rose shook her head, her mouth drawn into a grim line. She grabbed an umbrella from the stand next to the door and put her own hand on the door handle. They listened for a moment, but the ringing had stopped. Rose waited another beat and then wrenched the door open.

They both stared out into the darkness. Every nerve in Margery's body was alive and readying herself to run back up the stairs, but nothing happened. She squinted into the night to no avail and, as she leaned forward, the porch light clicked on, blinding her momentarily. She gasped, and took a step back into the safety of the hall.

On the front step, illuminated by the porch light, was a vase filled with pretty purple flowers.

Chapter Eight

Waking up so early was never easy and Margery begrudged the alarm clock as it sprang into life at six the next morning. Especially after the nonsense of last night. She and Rose had waited for ten minutes in the hall until they were sure that whoever had been outside was gone and Gloria had made her way down in her dressing gown finally to see what the noise had been about. Margery had not been able to sleep easily after that. When she had got back to the guest bedroom, Clementine had been awake and worried about where she'd been and why the doorbell had been ringing, and Margery had recounted the tale of the strange, unseen visitor who had left the flowers. Clementine had found it as bizarre as she had. Rose, to her credit, had not shown her surprise, putting on her bravest face and taking the flowers from the doorstep to plonk on the kitchen table. If she thought it was strange too, she had not said so, though she had admitted that she had no idea who would have left them there. There was something familiar about the flowers, but in the haze of the mayor's death and the hen party planning, Margery could not place them.

Eventually, Margery and Clementine managed to drag themselves up and get dressed, and before long they were hightailing it to the village. It was much colder than an August morning should be in Margery's opinion, and she pulled her cardigan close to herself as they walked over the dewy lawn to the car. The sprawling fields glowed as they zipped past them, the car's headlights cutting through the morning mist with its yellow beams. The village made up for the chill by being even prettier in the early morning light, the roads tranquil and still, the stone cottages they passed all with dark windows. Clementine directed them to the address Ceri-Ann had helped her to find and before Margery knew it, they found themselves in a car park outside a small warehouse in an industrial estate a mile or so away from the village. They stepped out of the car. The birds had finished their dawn chorus, but still twittered from the trees lining the route.

'Are you sure this is it?' Margery asked, squinting in the light from the sun, which was rising above them. Clementine didn't have to answer. Margery had barely finished speaking when the main warehouse door began to open slowly, the shutters squeaking as they rolled up and over. A green transit van reversed out. The logo on the side said 'Broc 'n' Roll Greengrocer's', along with a big cartoon depiction of a very happy head of broccoli.

Bingo, Margery thought to herself. They watched as the van continued to back into the car park. It slammed on its brakes, the brake lights bright and jarring in the early morning glow. Margery took a step back unconsciously.

'What on earth! Margery? Clem?' The driver rolled down their window and called out to them. 'Is that you?'

'Well, what on earth are you doing here?' Margery almost laughed as the figure leaped out of the van and strode over to them. Bizarrely – and in the last place Margery would have ever thought to look for her – was Doreen Rolley. Doreen had supplied the school kitchen with fruit and vegetables years before until she was outpriced by a newer greengrocer and had left Dewstow in a huff. Margery smiled at her. She had always enjoyed Doreen's sense of humour. It was good to see her.

'Doreen!' Clementine beamed as Doreen drew her in for a hug. 'How are you?'

'I'm fantastic.' Doreen beamed back. She looked fantastic too. She had not been young when she had supplied the school a decade ago, but she looked much the same, and in the same tatty overalls she had always worn. Margery marvelled at her; she looked positively spritely compared to them and they were only in their sixties. Her hair was as grey as Clementine's still but moving villages had obviously done her a world of good. Her skin had a healthy glow and she had retained the permanent twinkle she had always seemed to have in her eye. Doreen beamed at them both. 'God, I heard about Caroline and what happened! How are you?'

'We're okay.' Margery felt her smile fading a little as she remembered their first case – solving the untimely murder of their own kitchen manager. Doreen seemed to notice.

'Well, it's lovely to see you all the same. What brings you to this neck of the woods? You've got to be busy with that detective agency of yours.' She winked at Margery.

'You've heard about that, have you?' Margery asked, surprised.

'Of course, I still keep up with Dewstow – I get the Dewstow paper delivered here.' Doreen smiled at her again. 'I can't believe all that at Christmas! Gosh, you must both be ever so clever to work all of that out. Saved the school play, and most of the staff from what I read!'

'Something like that.' Margery grinned, suddenly feeling a bit shy. She decided not to tell Doreen what a mess they had made of that case before solving it at the last minute.

'We're on holiday!' Clementine said excitedly, answering Doreen's original question. 'And we have to do Rose's hen do.'

'Rose Smith is getting married?' Doreen looked at them both, her brow furrowed. 'Isn't she already married?'

'It's a long story,' Margery said. Doreen rolled her eyes. Doreen and Rose went way back too. They'd known each other for a decade or so; Doreen had been part of her amateur dramatics club that she held on Wednesday nights in the church hall.

'Always a long story with that one.' She laughed, leaning back against the van. 'Remember when she threw a satsuma at Caroline because you ran out of egg mayonnaise sandwiches?'

'I do.' Margery chuckled too. It was nice to see Doreen and to reminisce about the past. It had been a long time. When they had gone to her leaving drinks at the Bell and Hope, they had promised to stay in touch, but as the years passed that had fallen by the wayside. This was the last place she had ever thought they would meet again.

'I can't believe you ended up here,' Clementine said, as though she had read Margery's mind. 'In St Martin's of all places – why St Martin's, anyway? It's a bit out of the way, isn't it?'

'Well, it's not too far, is it? Only an hour down the motorway, if that,' Doreen explained. 'Close enough to see my grandchildren enough but not close enough to have to babysit constantly.' She laughed uproariously again at her own joke. 'Look, I've got to get off on my deliveries,' Doreen said, gesturing to the van she was leaning against. 'Can I get you anything? An apple? A satsuma? Gosh, I never ever asked why you're here!'

'That's a long story as well,' Margery said. 'It involves The Boar's Head hotel and what we believe to be some poisonous plants.'

'You're kidding.' Doreen's mouth was hanging open. 'You're not involved in that, are you?'

'You know about it?'

'Of course. The police have already been down here, going through my warehouse.' Doreen shook her head, her eyes darkening. 'They ruined an entire day's orders with all their poking around. There was nearly a riot at the Rose and Crown when they didn't get their potato delivery to make the chips in time for lunch. The chef was in tears when I got there.'

'When did the police come?' Margery asked.

'Yesterday morning.' Doreen rolled her eyes, leaning back against the van again. She seemed to have forgotten she had been in a rush to start her deliveries. Margery hoped the chef from the Rose and Crown would be okay if Doreen didn't manage to make it before lunchtime again. 'Came in here, snooping about. I don't sell stuff like that, I told them.'

'You don't sell sorrel?' Clementine asked.

'Not often,' Doreen said. 'Not much call for it around here and I don't do foraging, really. Not my thing at all. My body was made for sitting on the beach, not hunting about on the hills for ugly plants.'

'Gosh, really? But is there still a lot of foraging around here?' Clementine asked. The surprise on her face was palpable. Margery had never even considered it as an option. They washed all their vegetables. Even the punnets of fruit from the supermarket. Margery didn't think that eating the odd bug would be that bad for her immune system and she was always nibbling on the straw-berries she grew in their back garden, but Clementine insisted on it.

'Oh yes.' Doreen nodded. 'Loads. Not all of it ends well. They found hemlock roots on the beach a few years back. Some poor sap took them home and cooked them. Thought they were parsnips.'

'Gosh,' Margery said.

'It didn't end well for him,' Doreen said, smiling grimly. 'And it caused all these silly rumours about the poisoner being back. All that's started up again now as well, especially as I heard that it was lords-and-ladies what did it. Apparently, that was the plant the poisoner used to always use...'

'The poisoner!' Clementine cried. 'We keep hearing about them. Do you know who they were?'

'Not really.' Doreen looked tired suddenly. 'Happened before I moved here, you see. I've heard things though. Nasty things.'

'Like what?' Clementine asked.

She looked at her watch, as though she had finally realised how late she was. 'Tell you what, let's get together later in the week. I'll tell you everything I know then,' Doreen said. She reached into the pocket of her dirty overalls and handed Margery the small piece of card she pulled from it. 'Here's my number; give me a ring. I'd love to see Rose and get a few digs in too.'

She winked at them and then got back into her ancient van, the engine struggling to life once more. They waved her off until she had disappeared down the road and out of sight.

'Let's go over the facts,' Clementine said a bit later as they sat on a bench overlooking the car park toilet block, listing on her fingers. 'A man dies. One of the hotel staff disappears. The police act strangely towards us, Ceri-Ann reckons that the man who died was poisoned, and people keep telling us about someone who used to poison people decades ago, but they either won't tell us who it is or don't know.'

'And the hotel owner, Mr Warrell, might be involved,' Margery said.

'And the hotel owner might be involved, as well as some of his staff,' Clementine repeated, looking at her watch. 'And now we're waiting for Sarah—'

'Sophie,' Margery interrupted.

'Yes, my mistake, Sophie to arrive with some information and yet we've been sat here for hours, and she isn't here.'

'It's only been ten minutes, Clem,' Margery chastised her wife. 'Gosh, I hope we haven't missed her.'

'Ten minutes! We're getting on a bit now, aren't we, Margery?' Clementine stared at the empty car park as though she could conjure Sophie using sheer will. 'Ten minutes at this age may as well be six months. How long are we going to wait?'

'I don't know,' Margery confessed. She really didn't. How long were people supposed to wait during events like these? 'What do you think we should do? Go back to the newspaper office? See if she's there?'

'Maybe, but then Mrs Wainwright will probably kick us out again, won't she?' Clementine said. 'And I don't fancy being manhandled out of the office by an eighty-year-old again anyway.'

She kicked the stones scattered on the ground around them with the toe of her shoe. The weather had looked like it might be about to cheer up after the glorious sunshine the afternoon before, but it had faded back to grey again. The rainclouds were heavy against the sky and Margery pulled her coat closer around her neck in an attempt to keep the breeze out. It was not really working, and she was beginning to feel the chill. She was cold, and the wait for Sophie was becoming increasingly boring.

'Let's give her another ten minutes and then go,' Margery decided. The weather was making her more irritable than usual. 'There's no point hanging around here if she isn't going to bother to turn up.'

At that moment, a large Range Rover zoomed around the corner and into the car park, its brakes screeching as it lurched to a stop. Margery realised with surprise that it was Rose's car. She was sitting behind the steering wheel with a scarf around her head, wearing comically large dark sunglasses. Seren sat next to her in the passenger seat, undisguised. She waved over to them frantically, her face pulled into a grimace.

'What are they doing here?' Margery asked.

'Seren texted me to ask where we were.' Clementine scratched her chin. 'I didn't think she'd show up, though!'

Seren got out of the car, slamming the door behind her with a clunk and ran over, flicking the lit cigarette she had been holding as she did so. It tumbled onto the ground but remained lit, a little red light in the foggy morning.

'You've got to come back to the house,' Seren huffed as she arrived at their bench. She grasped for both of their hands.

'Why?' Clementine demanded, not allowing Seren to drag her up by the arms as much as the woman tried.

'We can't talk here,' Seren pleaded; her eyes were darting around, and she looked practically terrified. 'Come on.'

They followed her to Rose's car somewhat reluctantly. Rose's mouth was pulled into a grim line, missing her usual lipstick. Margery felt her heartbeat begin to quicken. If Rose Smith had not had time to put on her usual flawless make-up, then something must be very wrong indeed. Margery clambered into the back and slid over so Clementine could climb in next to her. She fastened her seatbelt instinctively.

'What about my car?' Margery asked nervously as Rose began to pull out of the car park. 'I can't leave it here; we only put twenty pence in the parking meter.' Rose slammed on the brake again.

'Go and drive Margery's car home, Seren,' Rose said. Seren's mouth hung open.

'But I can't drive!' she said, wringing her hands together. 'I had a lesson once, but they asked me not to come back after I clipped the kerb and a hubcap fell off.'

'Yes, can I not drive my own car home?' Margery asked. 'What's this all about, Rose?'

Rose looked for a moment as if she was considering just driving off anyway whether Margery's car was accounted for or not, but she stopped herself with what looked like sheer willpower.

'I would rather just leave now,' she said through gritted teeth.

'Why?' Clementine asked. Rose pulled the car into the closest parking space and turned off the engine. She reached over into the side compartment next to her and pulled out a copy of the *St Martin's Chronicle*, passing it back so Margery could look at it. It was the newest copy

99

of the newspaper, dated that very morning. The headline read: *Mayor Dead, Poisoner Returns.*

Margery found herself staring at it for far too long, reading the headline repeatedly, trying to make the words on the page make sense with the picture that accompanied them. Pride of place on the front page was a black and white photograph of a woman from years ago, still dark-haired forever in the capture. Margery knew her; she knew her very well, but it still took her a second to realise that the woman she was looking at was Clementine.

Chapter Nine

They huddled around the newspaper in Rose's living room. It lay where she had placed it as they entered the room, on the coffee table and no one had touched it since, as if it would burn them if it were picked up. The room was very much like Rose's sitting room back in Dewstow, except the television was ever so slightly smaller here. She had obviously had all her interior design done by the same company, though: the room was all greys and rose golds. It was like sitting in the showroom of a furniture store.

'Well,' Clementine said for the hundredth time since seeing her own face staring back at her from the paper. 'At least we know why everyone's been staring at me.'

'And that photograph we found in George's caravan with you in it,' Margery said. She took a sip of hot tea from the cup in her hands. 'And why Sophie took that photo of us.' She pointed to the photo underneath the article on page two, which showed Margery and Clementine in the car park, both wide-eyed and startled by the camera flash.

'I don't understand,' Clementine said, running her fingers through her hair, pushing it away from her face. 'Do you think that's why they took us down to the station the other day?'

'Maybe,' Margery said. Rose and Seren nodded. Margery reached out and read the first page of the article again.

Nathan Jenkins, 43, St Martin-on-the-Water's beloved town mayor, died on Monday night after dining at The Boar's Head hotel. Police have confirmed that the mayor died under suspicious circumstances, and that they have opened a murder investigation. This paper has ascertained that the mayor died from anaphylaxis caused by ingesting a raw poisonous plant known colloquially as lords-and-ladies or Arum maculatum to be precise. There have currently been no arrests, but police are searching for George Kale, 72, of The Boar's Head hotel, who they say is a person of interest in the investigation and any information on his whereabouts is much welcomed. Police have also interviewed village newcomers, Clementine and Margery Butcher-Baker, ages and address unknown. We at the Chronicle feel that this is no simple matter of kitchen negligence. Clementine Butcher-Baker's striking resemblance to Maria Glover, the poisoner who plagued the village decades ago, cannot be ignored. Who is Clementine Butcher-Baker, the mysterious woman who has recently arrived in St Martin's? Please turn to page 2 to continue.

Petunia Wainwright had certainly not spared any words; the article rattled on and on for another four pages and then finished with a twenty-four-hour police hotline to call if you spotted George. Margery could imagine all the St Martin's-on-the-Water residents waking up and going to get their paper, sitting and reading all about the new person who had arrived in town – a woman who looked uncannily like the person they had all called 'the poisoner'. She looked at Clementine's face and then flipped back to the front cover again. Whoever this Maria Glover was, they certainly did look alike. Close enough for them all to assume the photograph had been of Clementine, anyway. Maria Glover had disappeared in 1995, following the deaths of five people, including the police chief of the nearby town of Merrowpool, and the injuries of several dozen more.

They had shown Rose and Seren the photograph from George's home and both agreed that it was Maria Glover standing proudly outside the hotel with him, though Rose had not known who the other person in the photograph was. Margery thought if they could figure that out then more than a few questions would be answered. But she had not been able to think of a way how yet; the unexpected newspaper article had frazzled her brain.

Rose had shrieked at Seren to put the kettle on the moment they arrived back at her house and Seren had obliged. Now, Rose was doling out an assortment of biscuits from a dainty china plate as Seren poured hurriedly from the *Alice in Wonderland* themed teapot that Margery had once looked longingly at through the glass window of Ittonvale's branch of Whittard's. Margery and Clementine perched together awkwardly on the window seat while Seren and Rose sat opposite on the large grey sofa. Rose had been in full deputy head mode from the moment they had sat down, but after seeing the photograph on Clementine's phone screen, she had ramped up another notch.

'You're going to need a solicitor,' Rose said briskly. She thrust a custard cream on a plate across to Margery, who took it gingerly. 'I've got a good one; he sorted all my mother's things.'

'Oh, not him!' Clementine groaned, putting her teacup and saucer down on the coffee table. 'He was only good because he was in love with her. Besides, don't solicitors specialise in different parts of the law? I'm not sure a probate lawyer will be much use to us here.'

'He also got me all my money back in my divorce, I'll have you know,' Rose bristled. 'I'll give him a call. We'll need all hands on deck for this. Seren, where are the others?'

'They've gone down to the beach,' Seren said. 'I tried to tell them it would rain but they just took all the umbrellas with them.'

'Not my good umbrella?' Rose demanded.

'The one we got at Disneyland Paris, I think,' Seren said. Rose shushed her.

'When did you go to Disneyland Paris?' Clementine asked, her eyebrows raising. 'Together? Wait…did you go on Space Mountain? Did you buy the ride photograph?'

'We went to Parc Astérix too,' Seren said, reaching for her phone on the coffee table. Rose's eyes widened, and she batted her hand away from it.

'Stop telling people we went to Disneyland,' Rose hissed. The teacup in her hand sloshed hot liquid every-where as she nudged Seren. 'And don't show them the ride photo.'

'It was for Rose's pre-hen,' Seren said sulkily, moving her chair away from Rose so she couldn't spill any more liquids on her. 'And we did buy all the ride photos, but

Rose won't let me show anyone them because they made her take off her sunglasses.'

'Pre-hen?' Margery asked. 'Gosh, how many theme parks did you go to?'

'Well, I'm the maid of honour so I had to make sure we had a perfect hen do before the wedding but it wasn't perfect because I accidentally left my purse on the ferry, and I ran out of euros before we even got to Puy du Fou theme park...'

'It was certainly not perfect,' Rose snapped. 'And I'm still absolutely livid that there's a limit on bringing cigarettes back and you wouldn't help me bring any more.'

'Well, my bag was full of all the wine you wanted to bring back—' Seren began, but Clementine interrupted their bickering.

'Can we get back on topic please?' Clementine said. 'It's just a silly local newspaper article with a strange picture of someone who looks a bit like me; do I really need a solicitor?'

'A bit? She's the absolute spit of you,' Rose said. 'Anyway, it's just a silly article now. What if it all spirals out of control? Who knows what could happen then. We all know what small towns are like.'

'So apart from paying a fortune for a solicitor, what is the plan?' Clementine asked. 'Obviously they think it was me who killed that man, just because I look like whoever this Maria is.'

'I think we go to the police again; they'll know more about the poisoner,' Margery said. She had been thinking of returning to the police station since she had seen Clementine's face staring back at her from the front page. 'Then we can tell them it wasn't you.'

'But they obviously have it out for us anyway,' Clementine pleaded. 'Remember how they questioned us about it? They obviously do think I had something to do with it.'

'Well, the fact of the matter is that if they do think it was you, we have got to clear your name. Why don't we go to the newspaper office again?' Margery suggested.

'They're the ones who published this!' Clementine said, gesturing to the newspaper. 'They clearly think I did it. Sophie obviously didn't want to help us at all, did she? She never turned up to meet us and she helped the other one, Mrs Wainwright, write this article. She even took the photograph! "Mystery killer strikes again" indeed.'

There was a silence as they all digested this information. Margery picked up the newspaper and skimmed the article again. It started with the mayor's untimely death, which the paper said the police had confirmed was by poisoning and then quickly veered down into the past. Margery could not get her head around it. She knew for a fact that Clementine had not been the poisoner. In 1995 they had only just started working at Summerview school and moved into their house in Dewstow. They had barely spent more than a day apart in that entire time; even now they still barely spent more than a day apart. Clementine could not possibly have had the time to sneak away to a tiny village miles away and cause complete havoc without Margery having known. Who was Maria? And where had she gone? And why did she bear such a terrifyingly striking resemblance to Clementine?

'You know what you should do, don't you?' Rose said quietly, taking a Bourbon biscuit from the plate in front of her. 'You should go back to the hotel.'

'How will that help?' Margery asked. 'That sounds like a terrible idea.'

'You'll be able to find out exactly what's going on there,' Rose said, looking down at the biscuit in interest. 'For example, do we know if the police have spoken to anyone from the hotel?'

'Emily and Colin definitely,' Margery said. 'But we can't work out why they'd be so interested in Emily…'

'We need to find the other woman,' Clementine said suddenly, as if she had decided something in her head finally.

'From the photograph?' Margery asked.

'Yes, exactly,' Clementine said. 'If we can't find George and Maria is gone, then who is the other woman?'

'That photograph was from decades ago,' Margery said. 'Would she still be in the village? Are you sure you don't recognise her, Rose?'

'Her face rings a bell,' Rose said apologetically. 'I feel like I could've certainly seen her around the village, but I can't place her.'

'Well, what are we going to do now?' Clementine said, getting to her feet and brushing crumbs from her skirt. Rose glared at her as they fell onto the carpet.

Margery took a sip of her now cold cup of tea and glanced at the lonely custard cream resting on the plate on the coffee table. Clementine did not sit down. Instead, she turned to Margery and stared at her earnestly as though she did not understand why she was still seated.

'Come on, Margery, let's go and make a plan,' Clementine said. 'We've got to clear my name. I don't want any more trouble over whatever this is.' She waved a hand manically at the open newspaper on the coffee table.

'I really don't know where to start, Clem,' Margery said, hoping Clementine would change her mind and sit down.

'You don't have a twin sister?' Rose asked sincerely.

'No,' Clementine said, picking up the paper and staring at it. She paused, and then more quietly, she said, 'Well, I don't think so.'

'Any siblings?'

Clementine shook her head. 'One brother, but he lives in Australia.'

'No sisters at all?'

'None that I know of.'

'None that you know of?' Rose asked curiously.

'I was adopted as a baby,' Clementine said, in a matter-of-fact sort of way, though Margery knew it must pain her to say it out loud. She wanted to reach out and hold her hand, but Clementine was still holding the newspaper very tightly in her fingers. 'My brother and I aren't related by blood. He's my parents' biological child. So, there could be relatives out there that I don't know of. We had a go at one of those ancestry websites before, didn't we, Margery? But it all seemed very complicated, so we gave up.'

Margery had suggested at the time that they ask someone with a bit more know-how to set it up for them, but Clementine had not wanted to tell anyone they knew about it. Margery had respected her wishes, though she knew deep down that Clementine had always wondered if there were anyone else out there. Her father had abandoned them when she was very young, and then her much older brother had moved to Perth, leaving Clementine and her mother quite alone. She still spoke to her brother on the phone on special occasions and sent letters to her niece, but the combination of the distance and the large age gap meant that it was not a particularly close relationship. Margery knew Clementine had always been a bit jealous of Margery's own larger family, with its many offshoots of cousins and distant nephews and nieces, but the older they got, the less it came up in conversation. Now that Clementine's mother had also passed away, they rarely spoke of it at all. Rose was stunned into silence for once, the sympathy and empathy written all over her face.

With a bang, the door to the good sitting room flew open and Ceri-Ann was revealed in the door frame, her eyes wide and a lit cigarette in her hand as though she had forgotten she was holding it.

'Have you all gone absolutely mental?' she asked Rose, who shook her head instinctively.

'Have you?' Rose said. 'You can't smoke in here near all my nice cushions. Put that out!'

'Then why have you got bloody foxgloves sat on the kitchen table, you idiot?' Ceri-Ann continued her tirade, ash falling everywhere as she waved the cigarette around. 'Do you want a horrible rash or what?'

Margery suddenly realised what she was talking about: the flowers that had mysteriously arrived the night before that were sitting in a vase on the kitchen table. She got up and followed Ceri-Ann, Clementine and Rose fast on her heels.

The back door to the kitchen was open, the empty ash tray still resting on the little garden table outside. Ceri-Ann must have seen the flowers through the window and stormed straight in to see why they were there.

'They came last night.' Rose pursed her lips as she stared at the vase, not looking Ceri-Ann in the eye. 'James sent me them. He's so romantic, so mystery solved.' When no one moved, she sighed, 'There was a note.'

'A note?' Margery asked. She hadn't noticed a note at all, but it had been the middle of the night and she was exhausted. It certainly did make sense for Mr Barrow to have been the one to send the flowers, but why he did it in the middle of the night, Margery had no idea. 'What did it say?'

Rose sighed and reached carefully into the vase, pulling out the tiny piece of paper that had been curled up inside it.

'*A rose by any other name would smell as sweet,*' she read aloud. 'You're forgetting that James was an English teacher before he was a headmaster, though...' She squinted at the message again. 'I thought he would have written the full quote; this is only the condensed version.'

Ceri-Ann snorted. 'Headmaster wants you to have a horrible reaction to them, does he? I don't think so, mate. You're forgetting I was in his GCSE English class. He hates *Romeo and Juliet*! He said that he thinks they're both idiots. One lesson he just put on the Baz Luhrmann film and then left the room! Didn't come back till just before the bell rang for lunch.' Somehow Margery couldn't quite imagine the headmaster using the word 'idiot' in his teaching, but Rose's expression suggested that she had heard him express a similar sentiment before.

'Well, what do you suggest happened otherwise?' Rose spluttered.

'There's some lunatic poisoning people hanging about and you're bringing poisonous flowers into a room where we eat, mate!' Ceri-Ann shook her head. Rose took the cigarette from her and took a drag, forgetting all about her own no-smoking-inside rule. Ceri-Ann continued. 'Do you know what happens if you ingest foxgloves? There's a reason you can't buy them at the supermarket.'

They all shook their heads.

'They used to use it as a herbal heart medicine,' Ceri-Ann explained. 'It can make you go into cardiac arrest.'

Rose took out her phone and tapped away at it. 'I've messaged him; I'm sure this is all a misunderstanding...' Her phone bleeped almost immediately as the headmaster replied. 'Oh...'

'It wasn't him, was it?' Margery asked.

'No,' Rose said, staring down at the phone screen, wide-eyed.

'So, if it wasn't Mr Barrow who sent them,' Ceri-Ann said, 'then who did?'

Chapter Ten

Margery woke with a start, gasping in a huge breath of air. Clementine was staring at her in the dark guest bedroom at Rose's house, her brow furrowed in concern.

'Are you all right?' she asked, her eyes bleary with sleep. 'You were fighting the duvet. Woke me up with all your waving. Were you dreaming you were the Queen?'

'Yes. I was at my platinum jubilee. Charles was handing out tiny flags,' Margery said. The lie was easier than worrying Clementine with her horrible nightmare. She sat up in bed shakily. 'What time is it?'

Clementine glanced at the alarm clock resting on the table on her side of the bed. 'Half past five,' she said grumpily, reaching over for her phone and unplugging it from the charger. Her voice was still scratchy from sleep. Margery exhaled deeply and tried to calm herself. The dream had felt all too real. She had not had a dream like it for a long time. Sometimes, it felt as though her dreams were trying to explain something to her, but she'd never been able to work out what they meant.

She settled herself back down in the comfortable bed though she knew it was fruitless to try and sleep again. They had been thinking about staying at the campsite for a few nights, for a break, though they hadn't made their minds up either way yet. Clementine seemed to think it might help clear her head. She had been very quiet since the revelation about Maria; it was not like her at all.

She wondered to herself about the photograph they had found in George's caravan. He must have known Maria very well indeed. They had spent hours the night before trying to figure out some sort of clue from it, scrolling through St Martin's-on-the-Water's Facebook page to try and find the other woman in the photograph to no avail; it had proved incredibly difficult to find someone when you don't even know their name. Margery wondered if she simply didn't have any social media, but if the woman was still in the village maybe she wouldn't be hard to find the old-fashioned way. Maybe there was an older member of the St Martin's community they could ask, though that might prove an issue with the local paper splashing their faces all over the front page in connection with the horrible murders.

'What's the plan today, then?' Clementine asked. Margery reluctantly dragged herself from the bed and got her special hen party notebook from her handbag.

'Well, Rose wants us to get on with some of these bits for the hen and the wedding. It's not long away.' Margery scanned the list with worried eyes. 'But I just feel like we've got more pressing problems now.'

There were far too many jobs that had not even been started and they were only doing the food. She dreaded to think what Seren's list looked like as maid of honour. She hoped she was a bit more organised that they were; she would never hear the end of it from Rose if the party weekend was not perfect. She had demanded Seren send invitations far and wide, yet Margery struggled to believe that Rose really had that many friends, and the ones she did have were definitely not here in St Martin's. Rose did not seem to go out into the village much and she had owned the farmhouse as a second home for a long time, since her grandfather had died. Maybe there was a reason Rose kept a distance.

'Yes, forget that.' Clementine sniffed dismissively. 'No one cares about Rose's party any more. I was talking about finding George and that lady, whoever she is.'

Margery hesitated. The police seemed to have a handle on it all already. Did they really need to get involved and get themselves into trouble again? Surely there was enough heat on them as it was. Clementine noticed her reluctance.

'Well, aren't you a little bit interested in who the other woman in the photo is?' Clementine asked. 'And Maria? We look too much alike to ignore it.'

'I agree,' Margery said. 'I suppose we could go to the high street and ask around about the mayor and the photograph. And I'd like to read a bit more of George's diary. It might still tell us something we can use.' They had run out of time to read any further the night before after all their Facebook searching. Combined with the early start, Margery had felt her eyes sliding closed the moment they had got into bed.

'Yes!' Clementine said, picking up her phone to wave at her. 'I've been thinking about Colin Warrell too. The man died in his hotel, and we know Colin is not a very nice man at all, in fact! Remember what Sophie said? That he's her nan's landlord? Why would she help us just because of that? He must have done something wrong. I bet he's one of those landlords you hear about who ignore the rat droppings and pop a bit of paint over the black mould growing in the bathroom.'

'Sophie also helped print an article with a picture of you calling you the poisoner, Clem,' Margery reminded her. 'I wouldn't put much stock in anything she says. Though I am wondering if Colin might have held a grudge after Nathan was made the mayor instead of him, like Rose said; maybe there's something to that.'

'Andrea didn't seem to think so, did she?'

They lapsed back into silence. Margery could almost hear the wheels in Clementine's brain turning.

'I always wanted a sister,' Clementine said finally, folding her arms over her chest and rubbing her own forearms with her thumbs. 'Vincent was just so much older than me; we never had that sibling relationship really. By the time I was old enough to not bore him, he was grown up and moving out.'

'Do you think you could be related?' Margery asked her gently, thinking of Maria's mugshot on the front cover of the newspaper. They did look remarkably similar.

'I don't know,' Clementine said, an air of wistfulness in her voice. Margery had a suspicion that Clementine was holding back on how she really felt. She hadn't said much about Maria Glover since they had seen the newspaper, but Margery knew her well enough to know when she was upset. This time Margery suspected that her woes wouldn't be soothed with a cup of tea and a slice of cake though. Clementine jumped out of bed. 'Come on, let's go and see what we can find out, maybe see Sophie again.' Margery could not stop the groan that poured from her mouth.

'Really?' she asked. 'Sophie? Why?'

'Why not!' Clementine smiled at her. 'She took that photo of me. And she said she would help us, and she hasn't, has she?'

'Well, no.' Margery struggled to come up with a reason not to visit her. 'Where will we go? The newspaper office again? Maybe she's gone into hiding like George.'

'We could find out where she lives.'

'How?'

Clementine paused. 'No idea,' she admitted. 'Gosh, this is a mess, isn't it?'

There was a sharp rap at the door. Before they even had a chance to react, Seren had flung open the door, and was gasping for breath like she had smoked a thousand cigarettes and then competed for Great Britain in the hundred metres Olympic relay.

'What on earth—' Clementine began but Seren interrupted her.

'You've...got...to...come...downstairs!' Seren panted. 'It's your car!'

She rushed out of the room as quickly as she'd come, and Margery and Clementine followed her instinctively. They rushed through the house, down both flights of stairs and out into the front garden, where Rose was pacing back and forth, on the phone. For a moment, Margery could not figure out what was wrong, apart from Rose's grim expression, but then she noticed their cars. Margery and Clementine's little Nissan had been parked behind Mrs Smith's ginormous white SUV. They were both still there, but now all four tyres of each car had been emptied of air. Margery gasped.

'Oh God!' she cried. 'What?'

Clementine walked over to the car and kicked a tyre fruitlessly. 'Flat as a pancake,' she said, her mouth drawn in a grim line.

'Rose is talking to the police right now,' Seren said, gesturing to Rose, who had begun to march in a line alongside the lavender bushes that lined her driveway. As if she knew they were waiting, Rose hung up the phone and stormed over.

'They're very busy, apparently,' she spat. 'Someone's going to come over in about ten years. Look at my beautiful car! Do you know how much my tyres cost?'

Margery shook her head, still staring at her own flat tyres. They were not punctured, she noticed as she moved closer to the car, but all the air had been drained from them. The little plastic tubes that usually kept the air in had been pulled off, littering the ground around the car. This couldn't possibly be an accident. 'I think we should be more worried about who did this, Rose.'

'Well, that too,' Rose blustered, still holding the phone in a vice-like grip. 'I'm going to check the camera I bought. We only put it up yesterday.' She began madly tapping at the phone, finding the app linked to her new doorbell camera.

'It's a bit early for shouting, isn't it?' Ceri-Ann had appeared on the doorstep behind them, holding a cup of coffee and looking between them all blearily. She squinted at the cars in the early morning light.

'Yes, thanks for that, Ceri-Ann,' Rose spluttered. Ceri-Ann ignored her, sitting down heavily on the doorstep of the front door with her knees pulled up.

'Look, look, there he is!' Rose cried. Margery stared at the phone too. The quality on the camera was not the best, but neither was its location, hanging over the front door of the house. Christopher had climbed up there on the ladder yesterday afternoon and fitted it for her. They could make out the figure creeping past the camera's view but nothing specific about them. The person was tall and dressed in the expensive wet-weather gear that everyone seemed to wear here, and they were holding what looked to Margery like a screwdriver. They slunk past the camera and disappeared out of view. Margery felt a chill go down her spine at the gun hanging over the person's back.

'I knew I should have bought two!' Rose wailed.

'Can you zoom in on it or something?' Margery asked. 'Look, Clem, he's got a gun!'

'Everyone's got guns here; it's the countryside.' Rose sniffed but she played the clip again anyway. The camera was not good enough to show anything more.

Clementine turned to Margery. 'I'll call our break-down cover, shall I?'

Margery nodded and then wandered over and joined Ceri-Ann on the other side of the step, watching Rose still storming up and down the long, winding driveway. The dull morning rain had passed, and it looked like it might be a bright afternoon yet. Usually that would have been endlessly enjoyable, but Margery was too worried to enjoy anything now. The police had asked them to stay in the village – had someone made certain that they couldn't leave? Rose lived quite far from any main roads; whoever had deflated their tyres must have known the house was here. Margery stared out across at the fields forlornly.

'You know, I've been Googling about that plant you found at the hotel. The one Clem took a photo of,' Ceri-Ann said. 'Its proper name is *Arum maculatum* like the paper said, but people also call it cuckoo-pint.'

Margery made a noise of disgust as she processed the name.

'I know, gross, innit!' Ceri-Ann chuckled. 'Apparently it tastes disgusting too; it must have been masked with some other flavours for him to eat so much he died.'

'Really?' Margery asked curiously.

'Yeah,' Ceri-Ann said, her mouth pulled into a grim line. 'It's dangerous 'cos it causes allergic reactions. That's what sounds like happened from what you said too.'

Margery nodded. 'It looked like he was having anaphylactic shock; that's what the paper said.'

'Well, there's loads of plants that can do that. There's this one, ooh, what's it called? Diffy-diffa…oh hang on.' She took out her phone and tapped away at it. 'Here it is – *Dieffenbachia* – what a mouthful that is. Anyway, just touching that can hurt you really badly. But there's loads more: wolfsbane, monkshood, hemlock. Wouldn't like to be a gardener with all that around.'

'Gosh, I've only ever tried to grow a few strawberries,' Margery said.

'Yeah, well,' Ceri-Ann said, 'that's probably for the best. Clementine would probably have the whole garden covered in deadly nightshade without either of you realising.'

Margery chuckled. Clementine had finished on the phone and walked over to them, plonking herself on the neat lawn in front of them.

'All sorted?' Margery asked.

Clementine nodded. 'In a way.'

'In a way?'

'You don't think whoever put those flowers there did the car tyres?' Clementine said instead of answering her question. 'Seems a bit odd, doesn't it? Two things happening here in the course of a few days.'

'I want to know how the police immediately knew it was a murder,' Margery said. 'They were very quick to apprehend us, weren't they? How did George manage to escape them?'

They went upstairs and dressed while they waited. Margery slid George's diary into her handbag as they left the guest room, determined that she would read much more of it today. They returned to the front of the house and joined Ceri-Ann, who was smoking another cigarette on the front doorstep, her legs curled up underneath her. A vehicle was puttering down the long driveway towards them. The sun was drying out the mud on the road and the car was drawing big plumes of dust up into the air.

Margery stood quickly, nearly knocking Ceri-Ann's drink from her hands as she did so. She raised a hand over her eyes and squinted as it came into view. It was not a car at all, in fact, but a van. It pulled into the front garden and stopped close enough for Margery to catch a glimpse of the cartoon broccoli on the side. Rose, who had been slumped down on one of the deckchairs, jumped up immediately as the driver of the van jumped down out of it. Doreen Rolley stood in front of them in her overalls.

'What on earth is she doing here?' Rose demanded, turning to Margery in horror. 'You haven't done a click and collect order, have you, Margery?'

'You know we don't know how to do the click bit.' Margery shrugged.

'I asked her to come,' Clementine said, getting up to greet Doreen. 'I rang her and she's got an air-blow-up thingy so she can fix our cars.'

Doreen walked around to the front of her van. Rose was still staring at her, open-mouthed. She turned to Margery, her eyebrows raised.

'How many more people are going to show up?' Rose said, her voice full of indignancy. 'Because I can't have any more hangers-on here, using all my guest rooms. Drinking all my elderflower cordial...' Doreen held her dirty hands up. Rose glared at the engine oil on them. '…using all the good handwash.'

'Don't worry, I'm not staying! I'll fill your tyres and check nothing else's been messed with,' Doreen said. Rose made a noise of strangled thanks and went to sit back down on the sun lounger, muttering something about not being a hotel.

'Thank you, Doreen.' Clementine smiled at her. Doreen waved nonchalantly back.

'Any time! Let's sort yours first, shall we? Might have a bit more trouble filling up that monstrosity!'

Rose glared at her again, but it did not have any menace behind it.

'You don't know any of the villagers, do you, Doreen?' Margery asked her as she helped her fetch her tools from the back of the van.

'I know most of them,' Doreen said pleasantly. 'You'd be surprised how many buy my monthly veg box. Why?'

'Do you know the woman in this photo?' Margery gestured at Clementine, who passed her the phone. Doreen stopped what she was doing with the toolbox and put her glasses on.

'Gosh, that's an oldie, isn't it!' She squinted at the screen. 'The one on the left is the poisoner, isn't it? But you probably already knew that, judging by the look on your faces.'

'We did,' Margery said, thinking back to yesterday's newspaper. 'Do you know who the other person is?'

'Yep.' Doreen handed the phone back. 'Funnily enough she's got the same haircut now! People just pick a style when they're twenty and then keep it forever, don't they? Her name's Janice Hornbottom; we're on the same bowls team.'

'You wouldn't happen to know where she lives?'

'I do!' Doreen said. 'I'll take you there.'

–

Doreen drove them into the village and dropped them off on Janice's street before she returned to Rose's to continue fixing their cars. Margery wondered if she would have time to carry on her – now very late – workday. Janice's house was just off the short line of shops and pubs and down a very steep hill into a long one-way street that was lined with terraced houses all the way from top to bottom. They were all painted different colours, and Margery found herself enjoying the differences in the rows of little houses. It was an odd bit of road. Each house on the long terrace had steps going up to the pavement, with a little area outside each for bins or flowerpots. It reminded Margery of basement flats in old houses you often saw in city centres; she'd always imagined that the steps would be precarious enough in summer, let alone during a frosty winter. They found themselves standing above the front door of a house named Peace Lily, the name written on a wooden sign nailed to it. Doreen sailed past them in the van, waving and beeping the horn. Margery watched her go as Clementine ducked down the few steps to knock on the door. They waited. The streets were not busy, and Margery found herself looking around, trying not to stare in through the windows of the other houses. It wouldn't do to make eye contact with anyone sitting in their living room.

The front door of the house finally opened, and Sophie from the *St Martin's Chronicle* stood in front of them. She gave a squeak and then slammed the door shut in their faces. Margery and Clementine exchanged a surprised look. Clementine rapped sharply on the door again, much more vigorously this time, now they knew the object of their recent upset was inside. She pounded with her fists on it, nearly making an indent in the wood in her efforts. Margery bent down to try and peer through the living room window.

'Sophie!' Clementine cried through the letter box. 'We need some answers!'

Sophie obviously did not feel up to giving any answers, but Clementine was not dissuaded. 'Come on!' she said, still knocking. 'It won't take a minute!'

The door opened and Clementine nearly fell face first into the tidy living room behind the woman who had opened it. It was not Sophie. It could, however, have been Sophie in fifty or sixty years. Certainly, she was at least a decade older than Margery or Clementine. She had the same sort of face as Sophie: very small and heart-shaped but her hair was no longer brown, but silver, and her glasses were not quite as thick. The woman eyed Clementine's face with great interest and then seemed to notice Margery standing behind her on the raised pave-ment. They stared back at the woman they had seen in the photograph from George's house. Doreen had been right.

'Margery and Clementine, is it?' the old woman said with a hint of a Yorkshire accent, the corners of her mouth curling up into a strange, misshapen smile. 'You'd both better come in.'

Chapter Eleven

The woman led them down a few steps and into the cool living room behind her, where Sophie was wringing her hands anxiously near the door that led into a warm and bright-looking kitchen. The sitting room itself was small, but impeccably well decorated. There seemed to be an enormous number of trinkets and decorative plates and clocks, but they all had their own tidy space among the squashy-looking sofa and matching chair. The seats were facing towards a tiny boxy television in the very corner of the room by the window as they entered. It was resting on a television cabinet with a VHS and DVD combination player directly underneath it. A small number of video tapes were on the left of it, arranged neatly and obviously well used. To the right were two DVDs that were still in their cellophane wrappers – the third *Shrek* film and *The King's Speech* – and to the left a large bookcase before the staircase, full to the brim with large tomes all about gardening. The window only revealed people's feet as they wandered down the street outside. Margery felt as though they were in a high-ceilinged cave. The walls were covered in watercolour paintings of plants and flowers. It was old, and Janice had obviously lived here for a very long time. There was a fresh coat of paint on the walls, but the colour was coming through from underneath, like patchy buttercream on a cake.

'Don't just stand there, girl,' the woman said to Sophie. 'Get these ladies some tea!'

Sophie jumped to attention and rushed into the kitchen. Margery could hear her clattering about in there and hoped that their arrival had not caused her too much trouble.

'Sit.' The woman gestured for Margery and Clementine to take a perch on the old sofa, and they did. She sat down opposite them heavily in the tatty chair. She was still smiling the same smile she had worn when she invited them inside, but Margery could tell that her pinched face was sizing them up behind her glasses. 'I'm Janice Hornbottom; Sophie is my granddaughter, though you've probably worked that out by now, haven't you?'

Margery started to ask, 'Did you work for George—'

'There'll be time for that,' Janice said, though she raised her eyebrows in a way that made Margery suspect she had not been expecting this line of questioning. 'Let's have a nice drink first, shall we? Get to know each other a bit.'

They stared at each other awkwardly, until Janice cleared her throat. Janice did not let the silence go on for long. She seemed like a woman who had no desire for it in her life.

'I can't believe you how much you look like her, Clementine. Gave me a right fright when Sophie showed me the photo of you both!' she started.

Sophie arrived back in the room with a teapot and placed it down on the coffee table between them. Margery gave her a weak smile in thanks. Sophie passed out steaming hot cups of tea. Margery looked between her and her grandmother curiously.

'Always so helpful, aren't you, Sophie?' Janice smiled at her granddaughter this time, showing off. Margery found herself feeling even more uneasy than she had when they had first entered the house.

Sophie nodded meekly and sat down on the arm of her grandmother's chair.

Janice laughed. 'Gosh, look at your faces – it's all right. I'm allowed to ask her to do things for me; she's my youngest granddaughter!'

Margery took a sip of the scalding liquid from the cup. She needed something to do while she processed this strange conversation.

'Fine,' Janice said, when she realised that neither Margery nor Clementine were going to react. Margery snuck a look at Clementine from the corner of her eye and realised that she was frozen, staring at Janice. 'I suppose I'd best tell you what I know, hadn't I?' Janice asked, finally lowering her voice from the level it had been at previously. 'You're here to ask about the poisoner.'

'Well, yes?' Clementine stared at the woman sitting across from them. Janice smiled again, much more grimly this time. 'We've been looking for you.'

'I guessed that. As soon as I saw your face, I knew that's what you were here for, and then your friend confirmed it for me.' She looked sympathetic. 'Since Sophie told me about you, I wondered if you'd turn up. I was hoping you wouldn't, though, I have to tell you.'

'Margery is my wife and yes, well,' Clementine spluttered through a mouthful of tea. 'What was all that about, Sophie? Printing my picture like that?'

Sophie looked startled again for a moment before she regained control of her emotions enough to babble. 'I'm sorry. Petunia said how much you looked like her and that it would be a good story and then she said she'd let me write it. She never lets me write anything! I've been begging her for months, and so I had to take the photo or she'd think I wasn't serious about wanting it. I was planning on showing her I had it and then deleting it, tell her the memory card was corrupt or something, but then she started telling me loads of stuff about the poisonings and the arrest and I just had to help her write the article.'

'What arrest?' Margery asked.

'The poisoner's, of course,' Sophie said, clutching her own cup tightly. 'Where the police all fell ill and she escaped. The village used to say she was a witch. Did you not read my article?'

'Of course we did,' Clementine said, though Margery knew that they had not. Not properly, in its entirety. They had been too concerned about hen parties and the mug shot that looked just like Clementine on the front cover to read the entirety of the article on the second, third and fourth pages. They had been half convinced Sophie had used the photograph of them as a nasty joke, but now she was seeing that the young lady sitting opposite them would not have. Instead, she had used it to further her burgeoning career at the newspaper. Both Sophie and her grandmother looked very uncomfortable for a moment, then Sophie stood and rushed upstairs, returning after a moment with an old and faded newspaper cutting.

'Here,' she panted, thrusting it into Margery's hands. 'All about the police station poisoning.'

Margery scanned the piece of paper; six officers had been taken to hospital after being knocked unconscious by an unknown substance. She put it down on the table in front of them and asked the question she really wanted to know.

'Who was Maria?' she asked softly. 'Where did she go?'

They room fell into a tense silence. Margery found it almost awkward to draw breath; her voice seemed so loud. The small room had felt so cosy only moments ago, but now it felt dark, oppressive and claustrophobic. She longed for the fresh air and the sunlight of the street outside it. Janice eyed them again; her face was pulled into a grimace. Clementine seemed lost for words; Margery could see her trying to work out what to say.

'Maria was my boss for a bit. At the hotel, I was just a kitchen assistant,' Janice said. 'I didn't work there long and we weren't great friends at any rate. I left a while before all the nonsense started happening, though.'

'Nonsense being?' Margery asked.

Janice gave her a wry look. 'Poisonings at the hotel is what I mean.'

'Wait,' Margery said, her brow furrowing. 'Wasn't George your boss?'

'Both of them were, really.' She seemed to ponder the memories as she drank from her teacup.

'And Colin Warrell was there then?' Clementine asked, her brow furrowed too. 'He was the owner?'

'He was.' Janice nodded.

'Mr Warrell turned up at the office yesterday and screamed at us for ages for printing about her.' Sophie spoke quickly, as though the words were forcing themselves out. 'Apparently, he and Mrs Wainwright had an agreement, and we broke it. But we had to tell everyone what happened at the hotel! What kind of "associate ambassadors for the village" would we be if we didn't? A man can't get poisoned like that and no one know anything about it. The more I read about the poisoner, the more I was sure it was the same person as this time. Mrs Wainwright was furious at him. She told him that we have freedom of the press, and had a duty to tell the truth and he would just have to put up with it.'

'Why does Mr Warrell care about what Mrs Wainwright prints?' Margery began but her words ground to a halt as her eyes fell on the thick piece of paper on the table. She leaned forward and looked closely. It was the original photograph that Sophie had used for the article. The photograph was much better quality in the original print; she could see clearly the tiny differences in the woman's features from Clementine's. Different eyes, a slightly less protruding nose, though Margery thought that maybe she was the expert on Clementine's face, after having looked at it every day for over forty years. The person printed on the picture in front of them looked so much like Clementine that a mere onlooker would struggle to tell them apart at a glance. No wonder the entire village stared at them everywhere they went.

'He cares because they had an agreement about Maria,' Sophie said.

'But why? Because he owned the hotel when she worked there?' Clementine asked, picking up the photograph. 'Why would he care about Maria now?'

Sophie and Janice shared a look, but neither spoke. Margery had the distinct feeling they were hiding something from them, but she couldn't work out what exactly.

'Sophie tells me that Colin Warrell is your landlord, Janice,' Margery finally said, remembering what she was going to ask, if only to break the terrible quiet.

'Yes.' Janice looked at her darkly. 'He is. For my sins. I'm sure I must have done something awful in another life to deserve that.'

'I'm sorry,' Margery said, though she wasn't entirely sure what she was apologising for.

'Oh, don't be,' Janice said, adding a sugar lump to her tea and sitting back with a sigh. 'It's my own fault really. I sold the house to him.'

'This house?' Clementine asked, finally putting the photograph of Maria back down on the coffee table.

'Yes. My husband, Bill, we bought it when we moved here from Yorkshire. Thought it were beautiful.' Janice's gaze seemed far away. 'The perfect retirement house, though we still had a bit of mortgage left, you know? We thought he'd get a little job to pay it off and I could potter and look after the grandkids when they visited. Family first, we always said, but it wasn't to be.'

'What happened?' Margery asked, though she knew without asking that the answer would not be pleasant.

There were no signs of Bill in the house except for a few faded photographs on the wall behind Janice. There were only two ladies' coats on the hooks by the front door and the shoes laid neatly underneath were obviously all Sophie's wide array of stylish trainers and Janice's comfortable slip-on sandals. Janice exhaled deeply and placed her teacup on the coffee table gently.

'Died young, didn't he? Just like his dad.' She shook her head. 'Cancer. Awful it was. He just wasted away to nothing. There was barely anything left of him to bury. Just skin and bones.' She reached over and patted young Sophie's hand sympathetically. Sophie had gone a pale colour and she was looking morosely into her own teacup. 'Sorry, dear. Shouldn't have brought up your grandad.'

'It's okay,' Sophie said. 'I wasn't born when he died.'

'Yes, 1994 it was.' Janice nodded in agreement. 'You'd have not even been thought of yet. But still, it's not a very nice topic. Anyway, like I were saying, he died and the house still wasn't paid off so that was a trouble, and he didn't have any life insurance either, so I didn't get anything much. Just the little bit of money he'd saved till his pension kicked in.'

'So, Mr Warrell?'

'He offered me a deal.' Janice nodded. 'I sold him the house cheap on the promise that I could live in it and pay him just a little bit of rent. I don't think I'm the only one in the village; lots of the oldies owe him rent every week. No point drawing the pension sometimes, I think; I might as well just put it in his name, the amount of rent he takes. Says he could get more from renting them out as holiday cottages, so we'd better pay up.'

Margery and Clementine both gasped.

'That's extortion!' Clementine cried.

'Well, he was a bad egg even back then, even after all that nastiness had happened and he was trying to lie low. But what can I do? I can't move now.' Janice smiled sadly. 'This is my home. Me and Bill's home and now Sophie's too.'

'But you'll have to pay him money forever,' Margery said.

'I know,' Janice said quietly. 'It's a terrible thing.'

Margery shook her head in pity.

'Sophie helps, though,' Janice said, nodding towards the young woman who had begun to pack away the finished tea things, though Margery had barely touched hers. 'She lives in the second bedroom and pays her way with her job at the paper, don't you, Sophie?'

Young Sophie nodded and disappeared for a moment to the kitchen with the empty cups. When she returned, the atmosphere had cleared a little, as though by telling the story Janice had managed to dispel some of the tension.

'That Petunia Wainwright ought to be careful what she does as well,' Janice said knowingly. 'She already owes him money on her rent. He'll have the rest of the house if she's not careful. He'll have her out and make it into a self-catering place for tourists, you'll see. He's done it before.'

'Oh my God!' Margery cried before she could stop herself. Petunia Wainwright must either not care about Colin waving the literal roof over her head or she really cared about getting the truth out about Maria. Either way, it was incredibly brave when she could have just stayed silent.

'I know,' Janice said softly. 'I know.'

'I still can't believe how much she looks like you, Clem,' Margery said softly.

'Me neither.' Clementine chuckled. She seemed to have found her sense of humour again. Margery looked at her with worried eyes, hoping Clementine was truly okay.

'Do you know where George is?' Margery asked.

Janice stared at her. 'Why would I?' she finally said.

'Well, he worked there when you were there,' Margery said. 'Did you keep in touch?'

Janice wouldn't look her in the eye. It was as though she was afraid she'd give too much away if she did.

'I've no idea where he is,' she said, and something about her tone made Margery not believe her for a second.

'There's another thing,' Sophie said suddenly. They all turned to stare at her instead of each other. 'It's been covered up for years, though; I only found out while I was looking through the archives.'

She looked to her grandmother as though waiting for her to explain. Janice took a deep breath. She looked to Sophie, who gave her an encouraging smile.

'The year he bought my house there were a few incidents,' Janice began. 'Mainly involving poisonings of the townsfolk.'

'The poisoner.' Clementine pointed to the photograph. Janice nodded.

'Exactly. You already know about the poisonings, and you know that after she was arrested, Maria managed to mysteriously disappear.'

'Yes, you said she disappeared – how?' Margery asked.

'Well, she just did,' Janice said, her mouth pulled into a grim line, 'without a trace, but sometimes people still report sightings of her. The most interesting thing was who the poisoner, though she was never convicted, had been married to.'

'Who?' Margery asked, leaning in to not miss a word. 'Who was she married to?'

'Her husband,' Janice said in a hushed whisper, 'was Colin Warrell.'

Chapter Twelve

'Colin Warrell has been married twice. The first died, and, well, horrible to say really but the baby died with her – pre-eclampsia,' Janice whispered gently. 'A while later he met Maria, around the same time he bought the hotel by all accounts. She ran the kitchen. All was fine for a while, I believe. All very professional.' She looked away from them and seemed to become fascinated with a stain on the coffee table between them. 'Then Maria fell pregnant, and they married very quickly. Took us all by surprise, it did! No one had even suspected they were together, and his first wife had only been dead a year. The baby was born, things started to go wrong, and I don't know much more than that, I'm afraid.'

Margery and Clementine sat in open-mouthed shock. For someone who kept saying they did not know much about the situation, Janice seemed to be able to tell them a huge amount. What a terrible thing to happen to Colin Warrell, Margery thought, to lose both your wife and baby at once. It didn't bear thinking about. Maybe that was why he was so cantankerous now; surely an event like that would sour a person for good.

'His wife was the poisoner?' Margery asked, aghast, when she could find her voice again. 'But her name was Glover, wasn't it?'

'She kept her own name when they got married. Had loads of arguments about it when I knew her; I think she did it on purpose to drive him mad. Very old-fashioned is Colin,' Janice said quietly.

The room was very quiet; Margery could hear the soft clicking of the carriage clock on the mantel.

'So, Thomas?' Margery asked, thinking suddenly of Colin's son and the conversation they'd had had with him a few days before. If Colin had another child, they were certainly not working at the hotel.

'Yes, Thomas is their son,' Janice said.

Clementine scratched her jaw. 'But you must have known Maria well if you worked together. You really didn't know anything about the poisonings?' Clementine asked.

Janice shook her head, still not looking up. Margery's first instinct was that there was more to this than she was letting on. She thought about how close they were to their own colleagues – so close that they had ended up on holiday together and she thought nothing of it. Something was amiss with Janice's story.

'No, not well,' Janice said finally. 'I knew Maria, of course. Everyone here knows each other; it's only a little place. But she was very standoffish, and it was a busy little restaurant. She was my boss; we didn't have lots of time for chit chat – she was too busy giving me orders. It was my little job when Bill was still here to bring in a bit of money. I only did two days a week; I couldn't know about the poison, could I? And you're also forgetting that I'm twenty years older than her – we weren't best friends who went to the pub together.'

'Gosh…well…' Margery processed the information. Janice looked aggravated, sitting in the armchair with her arms folded tightly across her chest and her jaw clenched. 'Do you think she could be back? Our friend seems to think so.'

'I don't know. More people seem to think she's dead,' Janice snapped. Her features, which had been so carefree on their arrival, had darkened. 'But if she is back then she's only here for one thing: revenge.' She hissed the last word like a kettle releasing steam.

'Revenge,' Margery found herself repeating. 'But why Nathan Jenkins? What has he done to her?'

'I'm not sure. He is the mayor; maybe she decided to go for someone with a bit of power this time. Or maybe it's something to do with Colin. I always thought she might come back and try and ruin things for him. Maybe she thought taking out the mayor would be her first step to framing him.'

'We've heard that the mayor had plans to work with Colin,' Margery said. Janice raised an eyebrow.

'Well, there you go then. Though if I was the police, I wouldn't let Colin off the hook so easily after all that business with him running for mayor. Or Dr Bell or George for that matter.'

'But why George?' Clementine asked.

Janice shook her head and mumbled under her breath.

'Mrs Wainwright says that she thinks George was in on it with Maria before,' Sophie said. 'She says he's probably run because he slipped up and killed someone too important.'

'Why now, though?' Margery asked. Sophie shrugged.

'Do you think she's dead? Maria?' Clementine asked suddenly in a small voice. 'How can you be so sure she's alive?'

Janice did not say anything for a while. Instead, she sat back and considered them with sad eyes. Margery watched Sophie fiddle with the corners of the photograph on the table.

'I can't be sure,' Janice said finally. 'But I can feel that she is.'

'The police never questioned you?' Margery asked. 'Even though you worked at the hotel with Maria?'

'Like I said,' Janice stared her down. 'I hadn't worked there for a bit then, and anyway I'd been looking after Sophie the night Maria disappeared, her mum backed me up.'

'Do you know how that police officer died?' Clementine asked suddenly, it was obvious to Margery that she'd been mulling it over in her head. 'The paper didn't say.'

'No one knows,' Sophie said, in a mysterious tone. 'He washed up on the beach the day after Maria disappeared.'

The conversation fizzled out and Margery decided that they should call it a day after they spent much too long a moment looking at each other in awkward silence.

'Would you mind if I use your loo before we go?' Margery asked eventually, eyeing the teapot wryly.

'Of course, it's just through the kitchen past the larder. You can't miss it.' Janice pointed in the direction of the back rooms.

Margery got up and wandered into the dim light of the kitchen. She walked past the table, which looked to be where the artist of the watercolour paintings created them, past the pantry on the right and found the door to the tiny room that housed the Hornbottoms' downstairs toilet and washing machine right at the back of the kitchen. She used the facilities, washed her hands and then exited back into the kitchen. The view of the back garden from the sink was blocked by a stone wall and Margery found herself peering out through the window to try and catch a glimpse of sunlight, coming to the conclusion that the garden must be at the top of it. It was a funny house, all be told.

Her eye was drawn to a package on the kitchen counter. It could only recently have been opened, judging by the wrapping paper that had been discarded near it. Maybe Margery and Clementine's sudden arrival had disrupted the unveiling. Among the mess of wrapping paper, there was a canister of fine and colourful loose-leaf tea. She found her eye drawn to one of the paintings hanging above the table itself, which was of a green plant with spiky leaves smothered in delicate green flowers. Janice had signed it 'J. Hornbottom' in the right corner and in the left was the title of the painting's subject.

'Dog's mercury,' Margery whispered to herself, reading aloud. She made it back to the living room and picked up her handbag. Clementine gathered her own things.

'I'll walk you out,' Sophie said. 'I'm meeting Thomas and Emily in the village anyway before I go to work, I'm going to help them set up Emily's market stall. Mrs Wainwright is doing a whole piece about George Kale. We usually only publish twice a month; we've had to ask the printers to print it specially.'

'A lovely lad, Thomas.' Janice smiled at her. 'He's proof that not all the Warrells are bad.'

'You're meeting Thomas Warrell?' Margery asked in surprise.

'He's my boyfriend.' Sophie grinned, obviously very pleased to be asked.

Margery felt her eyebrows raising in surprise. 'And he didn't mind you printing that story about the hotel and his dad?'

'Of course not!' Sophie gasped. 'He encouraged me to write it when I told him; he respects the journalistic arts, you see.'

Clementine snorted, though she tried to cover up the sound with a cough.

'He really doesn't mind you reporting on his mother?' Margery asked.

Sophie's smile fell as though she had never considered it.

—

No sooner than they had made it out of Janice's house and were back on the main street, Margery heard a voice calling from the window of the house next to them.

'Hello. Where are you?' Margery moved over and peered in, her eyes meeting those of the voice's owner through the window. 'Oh, there you are!'

The little old lady gazed up at them both, her hands on the bottom of the open window. She was so short that only the top half of her face was visible, her nose peeking over the frame. She steeled herself for the conversation that was to follow. In her experience, if someone opened a window to talk to you instead of a door, the conversation that followed would be very strange indeed.

'Oh, hello,' Clementine said. 'We just came to see Janice.'

'Janice, yes!' she said excitedly. She had a knitting needle holding the bun in her hair secure. Margery was amazed she still had such dark hair when the wrinkles on her hands and on her face betrayed that she must be almost one hundred years old. 'She's my next-door neighbour.'

'Yes,' Margery said agreeably. 'She is. All right, well, thank—' she began but was interrupted.

'Do you like the village?' the old lady asked happily, not waiting for a reply. 'My husband and I lived here for sixty years! He got diabetes and died, though.'

'Oh, I'm very sorry to hear that,' Margery said. Clementine nodded earnestly.

'I've been in this house longer than anyone else on the street. If you ever need to know anything, you come to me, I know everything! My name's Prue. What are your names?'

'I'm Margery and this is Clementine.' Margery smiled, Prue's friendly energy cheering her up immensely after the dark and strange conversation at the Hornbottom house.

'Nice to meet you, Prue.' Clementine grinned at her and shook the hand that the elderly lady stuck out of the window towards them gingerly. Her skin was paper thin, and Margery watched the bones made visible by the sunshine through it.

'Yes!' Prue said. 'You too. You come back and see me again soon, please. We'll sit in the garden outside and have tea!'

They left Prue and began the trip home. It was a long walk back to Rose's house, but neither of them minded.

They had both left the Hornbottom household in a bit of a daze. Margery felt that the walk might do them both some good, though there was sure to have been a bus from the tiny high street. The weather was a bit nicer for a walk today at least and she could carry her anorak balled up in her arms rather than tightly done up around her neck. It was much more freeing, even if the greying sky did suggest that she would have to throw it back on at some point. The rain had held back a little for the moment, though, and from here on the cliff top they could see all the way down to the beach. The sea below looked dark and dangerous still. Margery squinted at the dots skimming along the surface, surfers braving the huge waves. Rather them than her, she thought. She was much more of a sun person than water, though there was something very cathartic about watching them ride the massive waves crashing against the beach, almost laughing in the face of the hideous weather.

Janice had given them specific instructions on getting back to Rose's, which she knew as 'the old Smith place'. The easiest way, she had said, was up onto the hilltop near the hotel and then through the fields and across the cliffs till they reached the long path to Rose's. It hadn't seemed that easy to Margery, hearing Janice give them the instructions, but she supposed that they had little choice. Clementine seemed much too deep in thought to be concerned about their route home, and so they had begun the walk. They made it all the way to the top of the hilltop before they spoke again.

'What do you think happened to Maria and that police officer that died?' Clementine asked her as they made their way carefully over a stile. The marram grass was spiky as they brushed past it, and the well-trodden coastal path was hard to get a grip on, the rabbit holes easy to trip over. Margery had been thinking the same thoughts about Maria. Janice had not known the exact circumstance. She supposed Sophie was too young to know anything more than the records at the paper could tell her, but she wondered what Janice was hiding. She had seemed much too willing to divulge the entire contents of her life story to not be concealing something.

'Probably nothing nice,' Margery said. 'It's a shame there's not any more information about the trial or what happened to the police officer that died.'

Clementine held out her hand to help steady Margery as she slid in a patch of mud. 'I wonder what Petunia's going to print in the next issue.'

'At least we know a little bit more about it all,' Margery said as they ambled onwards at a comfortable pace. There was still plenty of light and they were both in sensible shoes; there was no rush to get back when Rose would just moan at them about Ceri-Ann being too loud or Seren existing. Margery was beginning to feel glad that they would be staying at the campsite from tomorrow, though she was already dreading sleeping on the hard ground in a tent. 'Hopefully Rose was able to speak to the police in the time we've been out and has some answers about the tyres and those flowers.'

'What a strange week already,' Clementine said. 'At least you don't also have an evil clone. It's like waking up one day and finding that you look like a serial killer.' She paused, suddenly going pale. 'Gosh, actually, I suppose that's exactly what's happened!'

'Well, she was never convicted, was she?' Margery said, swinging her arms as she walked. It seemed to help as they stomped uphill through the shaggy grass. 'Did she even do it?'

'Yes, I was wondering that, and how did she manage to poison all those police officers?' Clementine wondered. 'Surely, someone must know what happened?'

'I don't know. I just don't know.'

They paused at another stile and made their way over it, up into the next field. Margery knew they were going the right way. She could see the hotel now as it loomed into view, and they continued upwards, stomping along the thin dirt path that zig-zagged its way up to the top. A figure appeared on the hill above them and Margery felt her heart race even faster.

'Isn't that Emily?' Margery asked, peering through the grey mist that seemed to be rising from the sea and blowing over.

'I think so,' Clementine said. 'What's she doing out here? I thought Sophie said she was going to meet her and Thomas at the market?'

She was wearing the purple waxed coat done right up to her chin to keep out any future rain, though she must have been boiling in today's temperate conditions. Most of her face was covered by the flaps of her winter flat cap, not even a hair showing from under it. Margery wouldn't have recognised her at all, if it were not for the coat; they had seen her wearing it outside the hotel on the day they had arrived. They were both wandering the zig-zag of paths that led up to the mainland. Every now and then she would pause and scan the bushes as Rupert sniffed the ground, his big feet surprisingly agile on the wet, muddy paths. Emily had a gun with her this afternoon, but she didn't seem to be hunting. Instead, she was holding a large cloth bag she was filling with plants from the undergrowth in front of her.

'What is she doing?' Clementine asked, the raindrops dripping from her face as she spoke. 'Is she foraging?'

'It certainly looks like it,' Margery whispered back.

Margery took her arm and they crept away as quickly as possible, which was not easy on the sandy, beaten path.

Their feet kept slipping on it, making the journey hard work. Clementine's large sunhat did not make them any less visible either. It was still so windy that Clementine had to keep one hat firmly clamped over her head to stop it blowing away.

It was no good. Emily looked over and stared; even Rupert stopped to gaze down at them. Margery raised a hand gingerly and gave a little wave. In response, Emily raised the gun and looked down the scope at them.

Chapter Thirteen

They reached the house just as it was getting dark and the sky was turning to shades of red and orange. Usually, Margery would have liked to stop and enjoy the sight, but today they were too frightened and panicked to admire the view. They entered the house and Clementine made sure the latch was locked on the front door. Only then did Margery feel like she could catch her breath as they collapsed against it.

'Where have you been?' Gloria asked as they entered the kitchen. Everyone else was there already, sitting at the big kitchen table, which had been set for dinner. Everybody turned to stare as Margery and Clementine joined them, shattering the calm atmosphere around the dinner table as they fell through the kitchen door. Karen put down the serving spoon she had been holding and looked up at them expectantly.

'Are you okay?' Seren asked. Rose was looking between them, her brow furrowed.

'No,' Margery managed to say. 'Emily,' she spluttered, 'Emily from the hotel.'

'She's out there picking plants on the bloody cliffs!' Clementine managed to blurt out. The entire kitchen fell silent, mouths hanging open. Margery could not tell if they were gawping at the information or Clementine, who had maybe sworn twice in the forty-something years they had known each other. 'Out in the fields behind the hotel. And she had a gun! She pointed it right at us.'

'Really?' Ceri-Ann cried, looking at the pair of them intently, as though she were more concerned by their sweaty appearance than anything. They must have looked a state, Margery thought. They had run as fast as they could the entire way home, only stopping so Clementine could use her asthma inhaler a couple of times. 'Should we call the police or something? What if it was her on that camera with the flowers?'

Margery passed her the number Detective Penfold had given them. Ceri-Ann took the piece of card and began to dial the number on her phone, leaving the table to make the call. Margery and Clementine slumped down at the table. The others stared at them. Margery took a glass of water and gulped it down, hoping it would help reduce the flush she could feel in her cheeks. Clementine gazed off into the distance, deep in thought. The big bowls of spaghetti and meatballs steamed in the middle of the table, forgotten.

'What happened?' Rose asked, her mouth open so wide Margery could almost see her back fillings. 'Did she shoot at you? Good God!'

'Well…no,' Margery admitted. The gun alone had panicked them, but now they were back in the safety of the house it all seemed a bit silly. She wondered for a moment if she should stop Ceri-Ann from ringing Detective Penfold before they embarrassed themselves, but it had seemed too suspicious.

'Did the police visit about the person with the gun?' Margery asked desperately.

'Yes, they said that there are lots of farmers in the area, and the public footpath goes past my house. And there's no proof whoever it was actually did anything.' Rose shook her head, as though she did not believe a word of it. 'They don't seem to be taking it very seriously at all, considering the mayor just died.'

'They're going to the hotel now,' Ceri-Ann said, sitting back down next to Margery. 'Then she's going to come here and talk to you. She didn't seem that surprised when I told her what you said.'

To her credit, Detective Penfold did not take long to arrive, and soon the doorbell was clanging again as it had done the other evening, making Margery jump and Clementine wince. Rose opened the door this time.

'Hello, Tanya,' Margery heard her say from the hallway. She could hear a note of surprise in her voice that was not usually present. The first time Detective Penfold had been here, Rose had been busy on her computer and Margery and Clementine had left with her without much fuss. 'I thought it was you when I heard the name.'

'Hello, Rose,' Margery heard Detective Penfold say. 'Still coming here in the summer, then?'

'Of course,' Rose said, her voice echoing down the hallway. 'Funny for you to be back, though.'

'Why? I grew up here,' Margery heard Detective Penfold retort, their voices coming closer. They entered the kitchen together. Detective Penfold looked tired, the bags under her eyes purple and pronounced. Everyone else had already gone about their evening plans or was watching the TV in the sitting room. Rose excused herself, though Margery knew she probably wanted nothing more than to sit in and listen. She could see the intrigue in her eyes as she shut the kitchen door behind her.

'Hello again,' the detective said, sitting down opposite them. 'I won't beat around the bush; it's getting on, isn't it?'

It was. Margery could see nothing but the darkness through the kitchen doors, her own reflection looking back at her in the glass. They gave their statement and she listened and wrote and asked questions at the right times but did not seem to have any hope for any of it.

'Right,' she said as she put down her pen and stretched her fingers; there was an air of weariness to her tone that suggested their conversation had sucked all the life out of her. 'I've spoken to Emily and Colin. He's insisting that she hasn't left the hotel today and Thomas says she was with him the whole time as well.'

'Well, she obviously did!' Clementine snapped in outrage. 'She looked down a gun at us and she was collecting plants! What if they were poisonous?'

'Can you prove it? Any of it?' Detective Penfold asked her, her face serious in the dim light of the kitchen. They all fell silent, the clock on the wall ticking down the seconds.

'No,' Clementine said finally.

'Can you not just go up there and have a look?' Margery pleaded with her. Detective Penfold actually laughed.

'Look at what? I got the warrant to search the hotel, which we did the morning after the mayor died but we found nothing. And Mr Warrell was nice enough to let me have a look around their flat and there were no bags of murderous plants anywhere then.' The frustration was written in the creases of her brow. Margery could tell from her expression that Penfold would probably love nothing more than to rip the entire hotel apart. 'And unless another crime has been committed—'

Clementine threw her hands up.

'—and you have *proof*, then I can enter again under section seventeen with my team. I'll do that if it comes to it, but at the moment all I can do is warn her off. I'm bound by the law. I can't just go barging into people's houses.'

'That doesn't help us now,' Clementine said. Margery sank back in the kitchen chair.

'Well, good news is if some evidence turns up then I can get a warrant in a few hours.' She considered them for a moment. 'The other issue I have with warrants is that the gun you've told me she was waving about doesn't match the description of the gun registered to her or any of the guns registered to Colin Warrell either. I've seen their papers; it's all above board.' There was a tone of disappointment to her voice.

'What do you mean?' Margery gasped. 'Whose is it, then?'

'No idea, but she has a Beretta Classic shotgun that Colin bought her as a gift, and it doesn't have a scope on it because she doesn't need it, because he's "an amazing shot and taught her everything she knows"...' She trailed off, obviously bored to death by Colin Warrell's no doubt incredibly descriptive and specific explanation of the family guns. 'Nothing like the one you've told me about, though he did admit that Thomas is crap at shooting, never got his licence.' She smirked.

'What about Nathan Jenkins's gun?' Margery asked. Detective Penfold raised an eyebrow.

'Know about that, do you?' she said. 'Hmmm, I suppose it might be worth having a look at that report again, see what we can find.'

'Yes, that gun had a scope; we saw the photographs of it on Facebook,' Margery said.

Detective Penfold rolled her eyes. 'I wish everyone round here would let me get on with my job.'

'Can you not arrest her for having a gun that's not the one registered to her?' Margery asked feebly. Detective Penfold exhaled loudly like a kettle coming to the boil.

'Nope,' she said. 'Mr Warrell owns that land. If anything, I could have you done for trespassing. But I'll look into it; I'll be in touch.' With that she stood, gathered her notes and swept out of the kitchen, leaving Margery and Clementine sitting at the table.

Rose wandered in immediately after the front door slammed shut, nosily peering around the kitchen doorframe, Seren following behind her.

'All okay?' she asked, though it was clear from their faces that it was not. She turned to the woman lurking behind her. 'Seren, put the kettle on.'

Seren made them all a cup of tea and then sat down opposite them at the table, next to Rose. And Margery and Clementine recounted the events of the day to them, telling them all about Janice and Sophie and what they had spoken about. When they finished, Margery took the diary out of her bag, determined to begin reading it again.

'You'd think a book called *The Big Book of British Plants* would be, well, big!' Rose said, pointing at it as it lay on the table.

'We must have more plants in Britain than that,' Seren said, her brow furrowed at the very normal-sized book. It was only slightly larger than the paperback crime novels

Margery had brought with them to read over the holidays. 'There's loads of plants out in the garden.'

'It's George's diary,' Margery explained.

'Margery stole it from George's caravan,' Clementine piped up.

'We *both* stole it!' Margery said, giving her wife a friendly glare.

'Oh!' Rose put her glasses on and began flipping through it. 'Well, then...anything good?'

'We have to finish reading it,' Clementine said. The room fell silent again as they all mulled it over.

'Yes, and we have to find out what Emily was doing on the cliffs with that bag. I feel like they're connected,' Margery pondered. 'Maybe there is something in the diary that explains why Maria killed those people. Why is Emily out collecting plants? Especially now that someone was poisoned at the hotel.'

Clementine raised her eyebrows at her remark in surprise, but she smiled at her. 'Margery! This is a new side of you. Yes! We'll find her and blackmail her, take her for all her gardening money! Then find George and get him to tell us what happened to Maria!'

'No, that's not what I meant.' Margery felt her cheeks flush.

Rose sighed dramatically like a balloon with a slow puncture and took off her glasses with a flourish Margery found incredibly annoying. 'Have either of you even read this? It's not George's.'

'How would you know that?' Clementine took the book from her and began to examine it as though it would have George's name written in it somewhere.

'Honestly, Mrs Butcher-Baker, you need to work on your reading comprehension. You're worse than my students.' Rose pointed at the book. 'That is clearly written by a woman.'

'But how do you know?' Clementine cried again. Rose glared at her.

'*Went on a date with Artie,*' she read, jabbing at the diary in Clementine's hands with a well-manicured finger. '*He told his wife that he had to work late and we drove all the way to Truro so we wouldn't be spotted…*'

Margery grasped for the book and read where Rose had been jabbing. If this wasn't George's diary, then why had it been in his house?

Clementine took the diary and flipped through it again from back to front. 'That doesn't prove anything; he could well be gay.'

'Yes,' Margery agreed. 'And it was just on a bookshelf in his caravan. You'd think he'd hide it away a bit better if it wasn't his.'

'This is all nonsense; why are we worrying about this when we should be worrying about what Emily was up to?' Clementine said haughtily. 'I think she's in cahoots with Colin. I bet she was collecting more poison. We can't just sit here and let them kill another person!'

'Well, everyone else suspects George,' Margery said. 'Isn't that why he's run off?'

'Maybe she's working with George?' Seren suggested.

'He did help her with the gardening,' Margery agreed.

'You know what you should do…' Rose began. She had taken off her glasses and was tapping them to her lips. 'Well, what we should do, rather…'

They waited for her to continue.

'By the time the police get their warrant, Emily or George or whoever will have been able to hide whatever she was collecting from the field and remove it from the hotel. I say we get there first, see what they've got. If there's poison and they're planning to murder another victim then we ought to get in there first and stop them.'

'If the police won't help us, we'll help ourselves,' Clementine said, leaning back in the chair and folding her arms.

'Exactly.' Rose put her glasses back on. 'For all we know, any of us could be next.'

'Yes! You heard the woman, Margery,' Clementine said. 'If some evidence turns up then they can get a warrant, well what if we find them their evidence?'

'What are you...' Margery began, looking between Rose and Clementine in dismay.

'A heist, Mrs Butcher-Baker,' Rose smiled so broadly it lit up her face. 'Let's plan a heist!'

Chapter Fourteen

'I can't believe this place has reopened already,' Rose said in disgust as they sat in her Range Rover in the darkening hotel car park. It was not particularly discreet in any fashion, but Margery and Clementine were counting on Ceri-Ann and Gloria being able to cause a big enough scene to distract any members of hotel staff. Karen and Sharon were also waiting in the wings in case of a real emergency and had joined Seren, all of them wandering up and down the road outside the hotel on lookout. 'I don't know what the police were thinking; they should get a health inspector out to condemn it. That man died less than a week ago.'

'Maybe Colin Warrell paid them off,' Margery whispered from her place in the back of the car next to Clementine. 'From what Janice was saying, he's got enough money.'

'Yes,' Rose drawled. 'Well, money can't buy class.'

'You should know,' Clementine piped up from her seat next to Margery. 'I've seen you buying knock-off Babybels at the supermarket.'

Rose turned to glare at her. 'Don't make me turn this car around and go straight home, Mrs Butcher-Baker.'

'This was your idea! Anyway,' Clementine said, her expression smug, 'you want to know what this is all about as much as we do. And if you do that, I'll have no choice but to tell everyone about the day you swallowed a fly because you were laughing so much at a student who had fallen off their bike and your mouth was open too wide.'

'It was very funny! And he wasn't hurt,' Rose spat as she scowled at Clementine. She tapped her hands on the steering wheel in short, impatient bursts. 'What's taking so long?'

Margery had been beginning to wonder that herself. The plan had seemed simple when they had thought it up the evening before at the kitchen table over glasses of wine as the warm evening breeze had blown through the lavender bushes in the front garden. It had taken two glasses of the lovely Pouilly-Fumé from Rose's cellar for her to calm down enough to forget what the gun had looked like as Emily raised it and aimed at them. Ceri-Ann had made it all seem so simple the night before. She and Gloria would go in and sit down to eat, cause a ruckus somehow and then she would text Clementine, and they would climb in through the family apartment's window and see if they could find any poisonous plants or anything else that could mean Colin and Emily were planning some other murder.

Ceri-Ann could see no wrong in any of the plan, but Margery was beginning to see the flaws now that they were undertaking it. For one, through the gloomy car park, she could not see if the apartment window was even open. Ceri-Ann had had a plan for that, though. In the event it was locked, Gloria would sneak into the apartment and let them in. Margery had shaken her head at the time and asked what the point of Clementine and her breaking in was if Gloria could do the job alone, but she had been shouted down by the others.

Clementine's phone buzzed from the seat between them, and she grabbed it. 'It's Ceri-Ann,' she hissed as she read the message. 'She says they're sitting down for dinner and all the family are in the dining hall! Thomas is cooking; he just came out to ask Emily something.'

'Well?' Rose looked back questioningly. 'Get on with it, then. I'll wait here and give the signal if there's *danger*.' She said the last word much too excitedly for Margery's liking.

'Yes. One beep on the horn please, not your original and insane plan of Morse code,' Margery said.

'I suppose I can contain myself, even though it sometimes seems fruitless having learned it at all.' Rose looked like she was enjoying herself immensely. She had wrapped a scarf around her head and was wearing her usual oversized sunglasses; Margery had no idea how she would be able to see them to pick them up in the darkness later.

'Come on, Margery,' Clementine said.

She reached up and clicked on the head torch she had strapped to her forehead. Margery sighed and did the same with her own. At least they were getting the most out of them, and they complemented their all-black outfits with matching garden gloves borrowed from Rose's shed. Ceri-Ann had had them scrambling around Rose's sitting room through an obstacle course made of Margery's crochet wool, which she had pinned up all around the walls, until Margery had insisted that she did not think that the hotel would have a laser-tripped alarm system.

Margery let Clementine grab her hand and lead her out of the car. They crept across the car park and up to the window. Margery peered inside while Clementine scanned the car park nervously, the beam from her head torch bouncing around ominously. She still couldn't believe that they were actually doing this, even though she supposed that they had broken into one person's house already.

They tiptoed up to the building and peered inside the window. It opened into the small living room of the hotel's family apartment. It wasn't a particularly exciting room. If you didn't know its purpose, you would think nothing of it. Margery craned her neck to look around. It was practically bare inside, just a small sofa and a flat-screen television hung on the wall opposite it. It was the complete opposite to their own home back in Dewstow, which looked like they were constantly in the middle of hosting a jumble sale There was just a lamp and a photograph in a frame on the little table, which showed a holiday Mr Warrell must have taken with Emily. He looked very pale and grumpy compared to her standing next to him in her pink striped bikini with her arms around his neck, and old enough to be her grandfather. Margery wondered again what on earth she could see in him. Thomas slouched behind them both, sunburned and unsmiling. The photo in the frame next to that one was of a very young and much spottier Thomas in his school uniform, unsmiling. *Like father, like son*, Margery thought. She wondered if they would come across a photograph of Thomas and Sophie together.

'Well,' Clementine said, sounding nervous now. 'After you, then, Margery.'

Thankfully, the window had been left open a sliver, courtesy of the sudden warmer weather, and it was easy for Margery to reach out and push it up with her fingertips. It slid up without complaint and suddenly Margery had a choice to make. It wasn't too late to go back to the car yet and demand that Rose drive them back to her house. She turned to say all this to Clementine, but the look on her face changed her mind. Clementine needed answers, and so Margery steeled herself for any eventuality and began to clamber in through the window.

She heaved herself inside and stumbled into the room. Clementine followed just as elegantly, narrowly missing knocking the lamp from the small table next to the sofa. As it was, it still wobbled perilously till Margery reached out to steady it.

'Careful!' Clementine hissed much too loudly for a person in their situation. 'Don't break anything.'

Margery's nerves stopped her from making any kind of retort. She sighed, looking around the sparse room. 'Doesn't look like there's much in here, does there, Clem?'

Clementine shook her head. 'No. Where's all their stuff? It's like no one even lives here.'

Margery slunk behind her as she followed Clementine's lead, trying to keep her footsteps as light as possible on the plush carpet. They crept into the long, thin hallway of the flat, carefully passing the main entrance door as they slid past. There was an interesting photograph on the wall of a large group of people standing in front of the hotel bar, which had not changed at all, wearing Santa hats. They were holding up pints of beer, and underneath, the little handwritten plaque attached to the frame said, 'Boar Hotel, Christmas 1994'. Colin was there; Margery recognised his ears though his hair had been much more voluminous. George, Janice and Maria were among the group too, though Maria was not smiling as she had been in the photo from George's. Margery looked closer, her brow furrowing when she recognised Prue, Janice's neighbour, who did not look much different.

Margery peered into the little kitchenette as they went along, but there was nothing of note she could see. Just a small kitchen table in one corner and then a very normal-looking kitchen set-up. This room was much more lived in than the living room, at least; it showed signs of life. The fridge had all the usual magnets and letters inviting the addressee to visit their local GP surgery for some invasive test or other. The counters under the overhead cupboards were tidy, but busily arranged. Somebody in the household obviously drank a lot of loose-leaf tea; there were several dozen small glass containers with cork tops full of the stuff and an infuser teapot sitting next to them. The canisters all looked similar to the one Margery had seen at Janice's house the day before. Sophie had said she was going to help Thomas set up Emily's stall at the market; it seemed likely that these were the teas she was selling. Margery wondered for a moment if that was why she had been out on the cliffs the day before.

She rummaged through the kitchen drawers until she found a nearly finished roll of tin foil and ripped a piece off, opening one of the canisters and sprinkling a portion of the tea into the makeshift container carefully. She folded the foil and slipped it into the pocket of her cardigan. Perhaps with Ceri-Ann's help they would be able to discern somehow what plants were in there and see what Emily had been out picking. Besides, Clementine and Margery were partial to the odd cup of tea or two or three.

'Ooh great idea,' Clementine hissed from behind her, interrupting her thoughts. 'Come on, I've found their bedroom.'

Margery left the kitchen and hurried along behind Clementine. She found herself in what was clearly Colin and Emily's bedroom. They were obviously incredibly tidy people. The bed was made neatly and piled up with throw cushions; the products on the dressing table were organised in what Margery assumed would be order of use. Even the shoe rack in the corner was methodically arranged, each pair of shoes laced together and polished, ready for the next event.

Clementine was busily looking through the wardrobe, the hangers swishing as she rustled through the clothes. Margery opened the top drawer in the chest gingerly and tried not to peer too closely at the underwear she revealed. The second drawer held only T-shirts and the third only neatly pressed trousers. She put her hand in and rummaged around blindly but did not come up with anything.

'Where is everything?' she whispered to Clementine. Clementine had finished looking through the cupboard and was now searching through the bedside table drawers.

'There's got to be something,' Clementine said, the frustration clear in her voice. 'I can't see the bag she had anywhere.'

'I can't either,' Margery said, finally removing her hands from the drawers and shutting them neatly again.

Clementine scratched her head and they both looked around. There really was nowhere else to look once they'd flung open the doors of the wooden wardrobe and discovered nothing but neatly hung clothes and shoes.

'We've got the tea; what else are we really looking for?' Margery said as Clementine scoffed. 'A full written confession? She's probably got rid of whatever was in the bag by now.'

'I don't know! There must be something else incriminating, some proof that they killed the mayor or even something we can use to get Janice to tell us something more,' Clementine said, looking around in dismay. 'All right, you go and have a look at the bathroom, just to cover all avenues, and I'll keep searching. I'll look in Thomas's bedroom.'

They both went back out into the corridor again and Margery crossed over into the bathroom as Clementine went into the next room, which she could see even from the hallway was a young person's bedroom with its game console and brand-new computer, the floor littered with dirty clothes and the walls covered in posters of musicians she'd never heard of.

'This is more like it, Margery!' Clementine called. Margery shushed her, but Clementine took no heed. 'There's loads of junk in here!'

Margery rolled her eyes at the volume of Clementine's voice and looked around. The bathroom suite was obviously from a far-forgotten age when avocado was an acceptable colour for a toilet and orange was the ideal tile colour. Apart from the garish décor, it was as spotlessly clean and neat as the rest of the flat, apart from the shower curtain, which hung messily across the bath, and the hand towel, which was rumpled on the rail by the sink. There was nowhere to hide anything in here, Margery thought, even if you had wanted to hide something. She went to make her way back across the hall to join Clementine in the bedroom but stopped suddenly at the commotion from outside. The air was alive with the horrendous noise of a car horn being sounded that stopped as soon as it had started. Across the hall, Clementine stared back at her, wide-eyed, as they both realised the same thing at once.

'That was Rose!' Clementine hissed just as her phone began to light up and ping as a series of messages arrived on it. 'We've got to hide! They're coming back!'

Margery gasped. Down the hall, Margery saw the doorknob of the main door turn slowly. She stood frozen for a moment, her body waiting for her brain to tell it what to do. There was nowhere to hide in the bathroom; she would be easily seen through the plain white shower curtain.

Clementine reached over and grasped for her hand, pulling her back into Colin and Emily's bedroom and closing the door, just as the main door began to open. They looked around in panic. The wooden standing wardrobe was too small for them both, but Clementine tried to shove Margery into it anyway. She did not fit – it was too narrow – and so they stood panicking in the bedroom for a moment. Margery felt herself breathing so rapidly she worried for a moment that she might faint. The window of the room was long and narrow, merely a slit above the bed just before the high ceiling began, rather than full size, and there was no way either of them would be able to even reach it, let alone climb through it to safety.

'Quick,' Clementine said, gesturing to the bed, 'get under here.'

There were a lot of boxes and bags and assorted junk that people kept under their beds where Clementine was pointing, but Margery managed to squeeze herself under it, just. It was only after she was on the floor facing the slats of the bed frame that she realised that Clementine wouldn't have the same opportunity.

'But what about you?' Margery hissed. Clementine's face appeared at the side she had slid under.

'I'll stand behind the door; hopefully they won't come in, and if they do, you'll be safe under here,' Clementine said in a matter-of-fact manner as she kneeled on the floor and peered down at her. 'If they catch me, just try and get out without them seeing.' She paused and looked back. 'I love you.'

'I love you,' Margery whispered back as Clementine tiptoed to the door. Margery was left alone among the boxes under the bed. They waited, and waited, and waited.

It was already getting hot among the boxes and, worse, Margery was not completely convinced she was hidden. The ruse would be ruined if anyone even took a good look at the bed from the doorway and caught a glimpse of her panicking underneath it. Margery wondered how long they would have to stay hidden and what if Clementine was caught? What a stupid idea this had been, and for what? What did they think they were playing at? They weren't detectives, not really, they were just two stupid middle-aged women who had got themselves into hot water yet again. The police would surely have a field day, as interested in Clementine as they had already been.

The thought of being trapped for so long was becoming too much. Margery could feel claustrophobia beginning to take hold in the small space. The urge to roll out and jump back up to her feet was terrible. She forced herself to lie back, to try to calm her breathing. She looked to the side. She couldn't see Emily or Colin, but she could hear voices in the other room. How were they going to escape?

There was a crash from another room in the flat. Margery gasped; what was going on out there? Were they having an argument? She backed as far under the bed as she could go, till her she was fully squashed up against the boxes. A hand grabbed her around the arm, and she nearly screamed, realising just before she gave herself away that it was only Clementine.

'Coast is clear,' she hissed. Margery took her hand gratefully as Clementine helped her out from under the bed. 'We've got two minutes.'

'What happened?' Margery whispered as they hurried down the hallway and into the living room again.

'No idea, but the coast is clear,' Clementine said as Margery took a step out of the living room window, using the windowsill and Clementine's shoulder to balance. 'Ceri-Ann texted me; she says we've got time to get away. A few minutes, anyway!'

'Thank God!' Margery said as her feet landed firmly in the safety of the car park. She turned to help Clementine through the window. Rose started the car and drove towards them.

'Come on, get in, get in!' she screeched through the window. They clambered into the back, coming face to face with Seren, Sharon and Karen, who were all out of breath and squished into the usually spacious car.

'Hello,' Margery said, making sure to buckle her seatbelt tightly. 'How did it go?'

'How did it go?' Rose squealed again as they zoomed out of the car park and away from the hotel. 'Two, yes, two people came into the car park. Did you not hear me not doing the Morse code?'

'Of course we did,' Clementine said. 'We hid under the bed.'

'Well, good for you, Mrs Butcher-Baker!' Rose was apoplectic now and nothing would stop her rant. 'We've all been out here risking our lives! And for what?'

'I don't know,' Margery panted. They all kept getting flung together as Rose disregarded all the speed limits. 'What a risk for nothing.'

'Not completely.' Clementine pulled a pile of papers from her bag. 'I think I know why the mayor was here that evening.'

Chapter Fifteen

'Gosh, this is a lot of legalese.' Rose kept flipping through the contract Clementine had taken from the Warrell flat. 'I can barely read it.'

'I can't believe he was selling the hotel,' Margery said. 'And to the mayor of all people; what was his plan with it?'

'Probably flats,' Rose said. She turned to the last page and lowered her glasses. There was space for the signatures under both the printed names of Colin Warrell and Nathan Jenkins, but the contract had not yet been signed. It never would be now.

There was a bang in the hallway outside and Margery looked over in the direction of the noise just in time for Ceri-Ann and Gloria to come bursting into the room, their faces bright and alive. They were still wearing the eveningwear they had gone out in. Margery had thought the full-length gowns borrowed from Rose's wardrobe were a bit much, but she had been outvoted. Ceri-Ann slipped the long gloves from her fingers and pulled. They came tumbling off her slender arms, and she placed them both on the kitchen table.

'You got back all right, then?' She beamed at them all. 'We were getting a bit worried when that owner bloke disappeared for ages, but we got him back, didn't we!'

Gloria raised the gown she was wearing high enough so they could see the bruise on her ankle. 'Ceri-Ann tried to kill me. You should be investigating her, Margery.'

'What happened?' Margery asked, jumping up to get ice to put on it.

'She pretended to fall down the stairs as a distraction,' Ceri-Ann said haughtily. Margery could not help but feel there was more to the story than that.

'She tripped me down the stairs!' Gloria hollered. She glared at Ceri-Ann, but Margery could tell that it was in jest.

'I pretended to push you!' Ceri-Ann snorted. 'It's not my fault you actually fell.'

'You wait till we get back to work,' Gloria said, lowering her voice menacingly. 'You'll be on potato-peeling duty for a month.'

'I'll convince Margery to buy in pre-peeled ones,' Ceri-Ann said, her lips turning upwards smugly. 'Anyway, what did you get? From the hotel, I mean. I hope it was good because we're now banned for life.'

'Apparently the combination of the stairs and spilling a whole bottle of red wine was too much for them,' Gloria said, her eyebrows raised wryly. 'Though Ceri-Ann sat and ate all of her starter before she came to help me.'

'You didn't need my help!' Ceri-Ann smiled at her. 'And I was starving – so much heist planning and not enough snacks.'

'Well.' Clementine spoke up. She gestured at the pages on the table. 'We found this contract.'

Ceri-Ann and Gloria looked at the A4 pieces of paper, their faces falling. Margery smiled at them apologetically.

'I found this tea for you to look at.' She handed Ceri-Ann the little ball of tin foil. Ceri-Ann unravelled it carefully and sniffed at it.

'Ooh, that's nice.' She sniffed again. 'I think it's nettles or something. Lovely! Shame that doesn't really help us.'

'No, I suppose not,' Margery said, resting her chin on her hands, slumping in defeat.

Rose yawned loudly and then stood from her chair, stretching her arms out.

'I'm off to bed, ladies. Margery and Clem, you're sure you're off to the campsite tomorrow? I booked you a nice patch; it's got electric hook-up. Though you know you're welcome to stay as long as you want.'

'Of course,' Margery said. 'We've somehow managed to pack already, even with all this going on. We just thought it might be a bit more of a holiday after all this mess.'

'Are you sure you're fine for us to leave?' Clementine asked, half seriously, half-jokingly. 'With the murderer and the car vandaliser still at large?'

'Don't worry, I've got all your dinner ladies here to throw at anyone trying to attack me,' Rose joked, then swept from the room; they could hear her stomping up the stairs.

One by one, the dinner lady team all went off to bed too. Eventually only Margery and Clementine were left sitting at the kitchen table. Clementine picked up *The Big Book of British Plants*, which she had left on the table earlier, and began to read it again.

'How are you holding up, Clem?' Margery asked, stifling a yawn.

'I'm all right,' Clementine said, still scanning the pages. 'I don't really know how I'm supposed to feel, really. I don't know whether it would be better for Maria to be alive or dead, especially if we are related.'

'Because either way no one's seen her for thirty years?'

Clementine hummed in agreement, occupied entirely by the book.

There was nothing left to do, really, but to go up to bed and try and sleep it all off, Margery thought. She was about to suggest that they go up and enjoy their last night on holiday not spent in a tent, but Clementine gasped and threw her hand over her mouth.

'What?' Margery asked, startled.

'*Still no period,*' Clementine read, jabbing at the diary. '*Going to Merrowpool to buy a test tomorrow.*'

Margery grasped for the book and read where Clementine had been jabbing. She was right, this couldn't be George's at all. If it wasn't his, then whose was it? And why had he had it in his caravan?

'I know whose diary this is!' Clementine cried.

—

Sunday 26th December 1993

Mr Warrell was nothing but vile yesterday all day during Christmas service. I ended up going and staying with Joplin and her husband last night, completely missing out on the celebrations in the evening, just so I didn't have to talk to him. I'm lucky they're such good friends really. Most people would kick you out if you turned up on their doorstep on Christmas Day crying about their boss! I think she suspects what's really going on, though. She's always looking at me too sympathetically. Like I'm fragile.

*Colin and I have made up. He came over with
some flowers and chocolates. It'll take more than
that for me to completely forgive him, but I don't
have anywhere else to go. Artie's wife hates me (for
obvious reasons!) so I can't be seen near there and
Joplin's got enough of her own worries.*

*I'm going see Artie tonight anyway. Old times'
sake…or something like it.*

They had sat up reading all night and though Margery
was exhausted, neither of them could stop. It was too
fascinating to know that they were inside Maria's head
after all they had heard about her. It made more sense
now that they knew it was her voice, anyway. She didn't
seem so evil, not by her day-to-day thoughts. Most of
which were centred on Mr Warrell, who was fifteen years
older than her, and someone else called Artie. Colin was
the only person she hadn't given a pseudonym, which
Margery thought said something. She continued to write
recipes and scrawled cooking tips down the sides of pages
or drew plating ideas for dishes she was going to put on
the menu at the hotel, and how best to find creatures and
plants to cook out in nature. She was young and enjoying
working in the kitchen as the head chef, though Fossil
still drove her mad. Fossil, who they now realised could
only have been George. Margery felt that had a bit of
cheek to it when she looked back at the newspaper article
and realised that George could only have been just over a
decade older than her at the time.

Maria was still honing her craft and hungry for the
accolades and attention. There were other people too,
who Margery could not have named, but existed in

Maria's world, all of whom they had read about before. But Margery thought that they might begin to be able to put some of the pieces together now that they knew it was Maria's words and not George's. There was someone she called Artie that she went to see often behind Colin's back because Colin didn't like him. The supplier who brought her the first of the season's produce in exchange for home-cooked meals. The friends she went out to the pub with, someone she called Joplin who was her closest friend and soothed her after her constant fights with Colin. It was very strange to see her as a fully formed person living her own life, with thoughts and feelings and desires and dreams.

Margery could see Clementine growing paler and wider-eyed as they read together under the tree in the garden, but she could do nothing to stop it. Who was she to tell Clementine to stop? What if this was a long-lost relative, as seemed so likely? Clementine deserved to know where she came from, who she was. Margery could never begrudge her that.

They had been sitting in the garden for an hour already, after spending much of the night reading through the little book. It was hard going, and they had given up at around two a.m., only to wake up as early as they could possibly bear to that morning and begin again. They had to take it in turns to read the small, sloped writing in the book, occasionally asking the other what they thought a particularly bad scrawl might say. It was obvious that Maria had put all of her private thoughts in it, and despite the precautionary nicknames, she had never meant for it to be found, especially as it had been written in something so innocuous. Inside the cover of an entirely different book was a very good hiding place for such a thing. Margery found herself wishing she had done the same forty years ago, before her mother had read her diary and discovered all about Clementine.

'Margery!' Gloria called from across the garden to Margery's comfortable seat on the bench in the early morning sunshine, interrupting her reading. Clementine looked up with a start. 'Margery! Clem!'

'What's wrong?' Margery called as Gloria rushed over. She hurriedly put the diary to one side out of the way.

'It's Ceri-Ann!' Gloria puffed as she reached their seat. 'She's really ill! What if it's poison like that man died of?'

'How ill?'

'She's been sick all morning,' Gloria said, twisting her fingers around the bracelet she wore on her wrist. 'She's not even smoking, she feels so ill!'

'Are you okay?' Clementine asked; she scanned Gloria with her eyes in concern. 'You feel fine, though?'

'Do you think it was some of the food from the hotel?' Margery gasped.

'I feel fine, but I didn't get to eat anything because they kicked us out before I could,' Gloria explained. 'Ceri-Ann ate all of hers and most of mine, though; she said it was delicious!'

Margery and Clementine were up on their feet at once, racing back into the house, the diary forgotten for the moment.

Chapter Sixteen

They put Ceri-Ann in the back of Rose's car, with several plastic carrier bags just in case, and zoomed off towards their destination. Gloria had come along after screeching at Rose that she was Ceri-Ann's work-mum and had a right to be there for her. Rose had demanded that everybody else stay at the farmhouse, but Margery and Clementine had insisted that they go too. If this was another instance of poison from the hotel then it was vital they know.

Margery wasn't entirely sure that they should not just be taking Ceri-Ann straight to an A&E department, but Rose had informed them that the nearest one was a good twenty miles away in the next town and, given the windy country lanes, it would take them too long. If it was poison, then they needed to move as quickly as possible. Ceri-Ann sat next to her on the back seat, her face very pale. She clutched the plastic shopping bag in front of her for dear life. Margery hoped her face did not look too disgusted; it was hard to control your expression when faced with such a sight, but similarly she hoped her anxiety was not showing either. It would not do to make the situation even worse by causing Ceri-Ann to panic.

Clementine turned from where she was sitting comfortably in the front seat, after winning the jostle as usual, and eyed Ceri-Ann with grave sympathy. 'How are you doing, Ceri-Ann?'

'All right,' Ceri-Ann blurted out, going green again as Rose took a particularly sharp corner in the car.

'Maybe you should just concentrate on something else,' Clementine said.

'Like what?' Ceri-Ann asked.

'Um, I Spy or something?' Clementine said.

'I swear to God—' Rose began; Clementine opened her mouth to tell her not to swear but was silenced by Rose's angry side-eyed look. 'If she's sick on any part of my car and it was your fault for winding her up, you will be paying for it, Mrs Butcher-Baker!' Rose shrieked as she pulled down a long sandy lane and approached the house at the end of it.

It was very different to Rose's own, much cosier-looking from the outside. It was a small chalet rather than a house, single storey and entirely wooden, though it was not weatherworn at all. It looked rather fresh, even; the blue paint did not show any cracks in the wood. The small driveway in front of it was sandy too and Margery found herself realising that they must be somewhere up on the cliffs.

'Where are we?' Clementine asked.

Rose ignored her and clambered out of the car. Margery helped Ceri-Ann do the same. She dropped down onto the ground, groaning and clutching her stomach, taking the carrier bag with her for support.

'God, I hope he's in.' Rose bounded up to the front door and pressed the buzzer. Clementine, Margery and Gloria helped Ceri-Ann along in a slow procession behind her. Margery wondered who it was Rose was hoping was here, of all places. This did not look very much like a hospital at all. The front door opened slowly, and the man inside came out to goggle at them all; they must have been an interesting sight indeed.

'Hello. Don't I know you?' he asked Margery and Clementine, looking from one to the other in concern. Rose looked between them with interest. Margery had recognised him instantly as the doctor with the white beard that had been sitting with and the mayor and his wife at the hotel only a few nights ago. Though he must have been in his seventies, he was still very handsome, and the age lines and wrinkles around his eyes only made him look more distinguished.

'Yes, sort of,' Margery said. 'We were at The Boar's Head hotel the other evening. When Mr Jenkins died.'

'Ah,' the doctor said, with a note of understanding. 'Yes, terrible business, that. Poor Nathan.'

'Can we come in? This woman is terribly ill, death's door.' Rose pointed at Ceri-Ann, who still looked a terrible shade of pale. 'We would have gone to the surgery but obviously it's Saturday.'

It had never struck Margery's mind what day of the week it was. There must have been some method to Rose's madness after all.

'Of course, of course,' Dr Bell said quickly, ushering them all into the house. The front door led straight into his tidy kitchen. He sat Ceri-Ann down at the kitchen table kindly, moving the glass canister of loose-leaf tea from the centre and placing it onto the kitchen counter so he had room to work. He then rushed to grab his medical bag, which was placed carefully by the front door. St Martin's was the kind of place where doctors still did house visits. Margery noted that the tea was speckled with purple and very pretty; she wondered briefly if it was one of Emily's concoctions from the market. Ceri-Ann groaned from the chair.

'What seems to be the problem?' he asked Ceri-Ann gently, sitting down beside her and taking her wrist to check her pulse.

'I ate at the hotel and now we think I've been poisoned like the mayor,' she said, her mouth pulled into a grim line. To his credit, Dr Bell managed to hide his surprise well, only blinking incredulously once before he turned to the rest of them.

'Would you mind giving up a bit of space for me to work?' he asked, pointing to a door through the kitchen. 'Make yourself at home in the living room; it's just through that door across there.'

They shuffled out to where he was pointing and entered the living room. Rose shut the door behind them, while Margery stared out of the large patio doors. She could see now why he would live here, all alone on the top of the hill. The window opened out onto the cliff face and the beach was visible below, well within walking distance. Outside was a small table and chairs. It would be the perfect place to have a spot of lunch or a morning coffee. Across the cliff she could see the tiny cafe that she and Clementine had planned to enjoy an afternoon tea at before any of this had started. They seemed like such simpler times, though it was only days before. The living room itself was small and had the neat, empty look of a bachelor's apartment. The few personal objects that were there seemed to be afterthoughts, just a few photographs lining the top of the bookcase and not much more.

She sat down on the arm of the sofa next to Clementine as Rose and Gloria squished onto the other side, and they waited. Margery resisted the urge to get *The*

Big Book of British Plants out and begin reading the diary again, though she could not wait to get to the end of it. If it was Maria, then it would be very interesting to see if she went from talking about her normal day-to-day life to confiding how she killed people. The other thing that had been troubling her about it was that George must have read the contents of the book. He must have known the secrets written inside it; why did he have it, and why had he kept it after all these years?

'If this is poison then the police were right to question Emily the first time,' Clementine finally said. 'We'll have to call them and get them to arrest her.'

'Why would she poison Ceri-Ann, though? She wouldn't have known who she was,' Margery asked. She couldn't work it out. Clementine wasn't able to either.

They sat in silence again for what felt like a long time, none of them daring to speak in case Dr Bell rushed in and demanded they take Ceri-Ann to a real hospital. Rose took out her smartphone, swiping through it, huffing as she did.

'Bloody cheap cameras – I can't ever seem to get the system to show me anything,' she muttered. Gloria took it from her and clicked something.

'Oh, well.' Rose took the phone back without thanks.

'What do you want that for anyway?' Gloria asked. 'You made them all go and buy balloons for your hen, didn't you?'

Rose ignored her, continuing to stare at the phone screen.

Margery sank back into the comfortable sofa, letting Clementine lean against her. This felt like the first break they'd had for a while, the first moment they'd had without breaking into hotels and caravans, and she looked around the room at the photographs. This was obviously Dr Bell's bachelor pad, but there were a few family photographs lining the bottom of the mantlepiece. Several of Dr Bell with who must have been his grown-up children, all of them blonde and beaming at the camera, and another of a chubby blonde baby asleep in his car seat. The photo was old, she could tell. The peace in the room did not last long. There was a screech and Margery sat up instinctively, Clementine sliding sideways as she did so.

'There's someone at my house!' Rose screeched again. 'Quick, quick! Get your coats!'

'It's the middle of summer; I don't have a coat,' Gloria scoffed, 'and I'm not leaving Ceri-Ann here on her own.'

'Fine, you two!' Rose grasped at Margery's cardigan to try and pull her up from the sofa. 'Come on!'

'Calm down, Rose,' Clementine said. 'What are you on about?'

Rose thrust the phone in Clementine's face; Margery tilted her head so she could look at it too. On screen, a man in a green anorak was smashing the flowerpots that ran along the front wall of Rose's farmhouse. He was wearing a flat cap pulled well over his brow and from behind it was impossible to tell exactly who it was. The rest of his outfit was just as nondescript, leather gloves covering his hands. Strapped around his back was a shotgun.

'Do you think it's whoever left those flowers?' Margery gasped. 'What if it's Colin? Revenge for the police talking to Emily?'

'We've got to find out,' Rose said desperately.

'Go.' Gloria waved them off. 'I'll stay with Ceri. The doctor didn't seem that worried, did he?'

'I'll come and get you both later,' Rose said sheepishly as she ushered Margery and Clementine from the room. The kitchen was empty; Dr Bell must have taken Ceri-Ann elsewhere in the house to examine her. They rushed through and out into front garden, Rose scrabbling for her keys until she found them. They climbed up into the SUV and she began to reverse drastically down the driveway. It had been raining heavily and the wheels kept slipping on the muddy path; Margery held on for dear life.

'Stop!' The front door of the house opened and Dr Bell rushed out. 'Stop!'

Rose, to her credit, did stop and waited for him to catch up. He arrived at the back window of the car, panting and waving a piece of paper. Margery rolled the window down and he passed it to her.

'Meet me tomorrow!' he puffed, out of breath. 'I need to talk to you about the night at the hotel.'

'But…what?'

'Please.' His eyes were desperate. 'Meet me at noon near the tearoom on the cliffs.'

He jogged back towards the house, leaving Margery holding the piece of paper with his phone number on it and remembering what Janice had said about the police needing to ask Dr Bell questions. Rose began to drive again.

Rose swung her massive car into the drive, narrowly missing hitting Margery's car, and leaped from it without even taking her keys out of the ignition. Margery could not help feeling that she was either incredibly brave or she hadn't thought much of the shotgun when she had seen it. Margery and Clementine followed as she stormed towards the little herb garden that had looked so lovely that morning. Now all the pots were smashed and broken, shards of ceramic littering the concrete of the path running alongside it. Rose kicked at the shards in her sandals, her face livid. She balled her hands in fists by her sides and then stormed over to the house without looking back at Margery or Clementine. They shared a look before following. Margery was not sure whether getting involved with a very angry Rose could be considered a fun holiday activity.

Rose had only put her foot on the first step before realising that she didn't have her keys, and she turned on her heel and rushed back towards them. They jumped out of the way as if Rose was a bowling ball and they the pins. No sooner had Rose finally grabbed the keys out of her car than they all heard the sound of laughter coming from the path they had just flown down; it pricked Margery's ears like an unexpected stream on a hot summer walk. They waited by the car to see who would appear, though Margery did not think the vandal would return that easily. She was right; Karen and Sharon appeared over the horizon, jogging smoothly in an almost hypnotising rhythm. Seren trailed behind them slower and much less gracefully.

'What the bloody hell are you playing at!' Rose screeched at them, spit flying from her mouth in her rage. Seren stopped dead at the sound of her voice and Margery could tell that she was considering turning and running back the other way.

'We're jogging!' Karen said as they huffed onto the driveway. 'We've got the Great Bristol 10k next month, and we can't just stop doing Park Run because we're on holibobs, can we?' She said the last bit as though Rose had lost her mind completely. Margery thought that Rose would have steam flying out of her ears if it were physically possible to manifest your anger bodily.

'I was going to pack my running shoes for holiday but then I just laughed for three hours instead,' Clementine said, leaning on Rose's car door.

Seren finally caught up with Karen and Sharon and seemed to have decided that if Rose was going to kill her, then so be it.

'What's happened?' she asked Rose soothingly, as though she was a stray cat she was trying to catch. Rose explained breathily, Seren's calm tone soothing her. Sharon and Karen followed as they all went to look at the broken garden again.

'Can you not do a swab or something like that?' Sharon asked. 'Call the police and get them to fingerprint every pot?'

'I rang them on the way here and they said they didn't have anyone to send, and the culprit was wearing gloves on the camera!' Rose cried, waving her phone around. Margery had to duck several times so it didn't hit her square in the face. 'Told me to email them the footage, but it doesn't save my mint, does it? What will we drink in our cocktails now?'

'Gloria bought some dried mint.' Seren patted her arm with the very tips of her fingers. 'We'll just add a bit of that.'

'I can't believe you work in a kitchen!' Rose began to hiss.

'There's a shoe print there,' Margery said, interrupting her before she could go full rant. She kneeled to look at it more closely. It was an interesting print, very large with a letter G intertwined with a T that took up the entire heel of the shoe.

'Sharon! That's a *Grip Trail Boots* boot print!' Karen gasped and clapped her hands in glee, kneeling down next to Margery. 'Oh my God! I've wanted a pair of those for ages.'

'What's so good about them?' Clementine asked, peering down at the boot print in the soft grass where the pots had been. Margery traced the imprint with her finger.

Karen rolled her eyes. 'Only the most expensive and limited walking boot company going! Why do you think me and Sharon are still pottering about wearing these old things?' She pointed down at her own battered trail running shoes. 'Christ, if I had a pair of Grip Trails, I'd never take them off!'

'Me neither!' Sharon looked as ecstatic as Karen at her find. 'God, whoever did this has got fantastic taste!'

'Fantastic…taste?' Rose stared between them both as though everyone but her had gone completely mad.

'But how can you tell?' Clementine scratched her head.

'Well, obviously the little logo.' Karen pointed at the huge intertwined letters. 'They always have a line that runs along them too in a neon colour, just in case you get lost while hiking and mountain rescue have to identify you by your shoes.'

'That can't possibly be the reason.' Margery shook her head.

'It also makes them look great!' Sharon smiled. 'Ooh, Karen, a real-life Grip Trail!'

Chapter Seventeen

Thursday 3rd February 1994

I'm pregnant.

I panicked and told Colin everything and we came to an agreement. He's really, really happy, said we've got to start looking for a head chef good enough to replace me while I'm on maternity. He said there's no way he's letting me work the last few months of pregnancy and Fossil isn't good enough to take over. Too old and slow. What if I don't want that, though? What if I don't want any of it?

I know none of this is particularly orthodox, but when has anything we've done been? We're getting married next month, just sent out all the invites and everything. He said he can take care of us both and he's so excited to be a dad. Am I doing the right thing? Are we doing the right thing? I'm thirty-one but I don't feel ready at all. Why am I even asking a bit of paper anyway!

Monday 14th March 1994

Forget what I said last entry and I'm sorry I haven't written recently. I know you're just a bit of paper but sometimes I feel like you're the only one I can tell my secrets to – I suppose that's the point.

A lot has changed. We got married last week in a tiny ceremony, just the staff from the hotel at the registry office in Merrowpool. Then I had my twelve-week scan today. Ours really, the baby and mine I mean. So funny to see them on the screen; the nurse said they were the right size and all is looking good. I feel like we've bonded a bit. I'm getting less worried as time goes by. Colin has been great, so supportive and he really doesn't have to be. We had to go all the way to the big hospital in Treliske to have it done. He was so funny. He kept panicking about having enough money for the parking. He's hoping for a boy, but I don't care what they are, if they are happy and healthy. He won't let me paint the room yet. Says it will be bad luck if we do. I'm going to sneak in there and paint it anyway. It's not his to have a say about.

Monday 26th September 1994

The baby is here, I am exhausted, but he is so beautiful. His name is Thomas. Born at quarter past five, just in time for Neighbours, I said to the midwife! Colin was out shooting when I went into labour, but luckily Artie was there. He deserved to be there anyway really.

'You ought to take a break from that thing, Margery,' Clementine said from the chair next to her, jolting her out of her thoughts. 'You'll get square eyes.'

'Square eyes from reading a book?' Margery laughed, but she put it down on the little camping table anyway. 'You're one to talk, on that phone all the time.'

'It's imperative that I'm on the phone,' Clementine said, looking away from where it sat in her hand and turning to gaze at her coolly. 'How else can I check on what mad nonsense Dawn is doing in our house and confirm it with the Dewstow Facebook community page?'

'You need to stop looking at that community page.' Margery shook her head. 'It's bringing out a very aggressive side to you.'

'They need to bring back parking on Dewstow high street,' Clementine said seriously. 'People can't get their Greggs sausage rolls without having to walk there.'

'Has anyone said anything about Ceri-Ann?' Margery asked.

'Gloria said she was all right,' Clementine said, looking at the phone again worriedly. She had set up a group WhatsApp for all the dinner lady team a few months ago. 'I'm beginning to wonder if we should have left Rose's, though – what if something else happens?'

They were sitting outside the tent they had borrowed from Rose, which was as oversized as everything else she owned. The campsite was very nice, and a short walk from Rose's house just as she had said. They were a sensible distance away from the toilet block but not too far from the reception building, which also contained a small shop. At the entrance there was a van serving sausages and burgers; Margery could still smell the delicious scent of frying onions in the air from their pitch. The only thing bothering her was the weather, which had not improved at all in the past few hours. In fact, it looked as though this might be the worst day for wind yet; it billowed around them already, the plastic tarpaulin of the tent rattling as it caught it.

'I don't like the sound of that wind.' Margery voiced her thoughts, looking at the diary again and turning to the next page, which was a lovely-looking recipe for hand-picked blackberry jam. Margery had debated with herself on the morality of using any of Maria's recipes, knowing her history, and had so far not copied any of them down, though she was very tempted to.

'I'm sure it'll be fine,' Clementine said, looking at her phone. Margery knew she was not really listening. 'We've camped in much worse.'

'Have we?' Margery asked her. They had not been camping for decades and the last time had been in the South of France in the boiling hot August heatwave of 2003. There had been no worries about wind then at all. 'When?'

Clementine looked up from her phone finally. 'Gosh, Margery,' she said, scratching her chin in befuddlement as she finally inspected the tent behind them. 'It doesn't look quite like the ones in the erection section of the camping shop, does it?'

Clementine was right, it was definitely not supposed to be quite so saggy. 'What if we tighten up some of these ropes?'

'Could do...' Clementine said. 'What's going on in the book, anyway? Has she poisoned anyone yet?'

'Not yet.' Margery shook her head. 'But I'm trying to work out who Artie is; she mentioned once that he had to get back to the surgery, so he either works there or he was a patient. I wonder if Dr Bell would remember someone called that. It's been decades, though, hasn't it? She only married Colin when she got pregnant; before that she always spoke about him as her boss more than her boyfriend.'

Clementine hummed. 'It does seem a bit odd.'

'Do you think you'd want to know if you were related?' Margery asked. She gazed at Clementine, trying to see how the woman across from her really felt. 'How would you find out?'

'I don't know.'

'She said in the diary at Christmas 1993 that she's thirty-one; how old were you then?'

'That was the year we got Marbles. Now, she was a lovely cat, wasn't she? None of this eating us out of house and home like Crinkles.'

'She was lovely.' Margery smiled at the memory of little Marbles, who had been very much a sleepy lap cat and spent most of her days draped over one of them like a blanket.

'I'd have been, ooh, thirty-three?' Clementine stroked her chin in thought, finally answering the question. 'God, the longer I live, the bigger a calculator I need to work it out.'

Margery murmured in agreement. Sometimes she had to steal a look at the date on her driving licence to work out her age. 'So, she would have been a few years younger than you are, then. Maybe a younger sister?'

'I don't know how to find out, though,' Clementine said. 'I don't have anyone left alive to ask. My brother wouldn't know. And there was nothing about any of it in my mother's things when she died.'

Margery had a wild and sudden idea. 'You know, Thomas might be able to help with that – he is her son. Surely his DNA would match yours if you are related?'

'That's a very good point,' Clementine said, her face brightening. 'Do you think he might agree to do a test?'

'Maybe,' Margery wondered. 'You can only ask and see what he says.'

She kept everything crossed for Clementine that Thomas would agree.

They trailed off into silence. Clementine gestured for the book, Margery handed it to her and then Clementine opened the diary and began to read again. Margery sat and thought about Thomas. Maria had looked so much like Clementine; if they were related, then Thomas was a window into what a child of Clementine's might have looked like if she had ever had any. She shook the thought away as quickly as it had arrived. It didn't do to dwell on things that had never happened.

'God, listen to this, Margery: "Colin bought Joplin's house. I said I thought it was a bad idea, but he wouldn't listen. Too much money and not enough sense, I said. Joplin is not talking to me. I hope she doesn't think I had anything to do with it."' They looked at each other, eyebrows raised.

'Skip forward a bit,' Margery said. 'Gosh, I wish we knew who Joplin was.'

'Joplin is obviously Janice,' Clementine said with a dismissive wave.

Margery brought her own hand to her forehead. 'Of course! Janis Joplin! I wish Maria hadn't written it all so cryptically.'

Clementine flipped forward a few pages, skipping to a random entry. Margery read over her shoulder.

Saturday 18th February 1995

A man fell ill in the hotel restaurant. He just keeled over and had to go to hospital. The police have been in, but they could not find anything

*wrong in the kitchen. Between Fossil and I, we
keep it nice and tidy. They blamed a bad batch of
vegetables. Though I do not see how that could be
as I'd picked them that morning!*

'Do you find it a bit odd…' Margery paused as she tried to
think how to word her accusation. 'That these poisonings
started happening after Janice sold her house to Colin?'

'Yes, I do,' Clementine agreed, still flipping through.
'There's still so many entries, Margery.' There were. All of
them written in Maria's tiny scrawl.

Margery was amazed neither of them had strained their
eyes squinting at them in the dim light of the darkening
sky.

'What's the last one say?' she breathed. Clementine
turned the book over and opened the last page.

Thursday 1ˢᵗ June 1995

*Colin has handed me in! He told them he thinks it
was me! I am leaving with Thomas – I could get
away much easier without him, but I can't leave
my baby. We are leaving now. I've got to get away
as fast as I can and confront*

The scrawl finished there, mid-sentence. Clementine
carefully checked that there were no other pages and then
closed it again. They sat quietly for a moment, processing
the information.

'Do you think the police came for her and interrupted her?' Clementine whispered. 'Who was she going
to confront?'

'I'm not sure,' Margery said honestly. 'Wouldn't the
police have found the book if they did?'

'Well, she can't have got away with the baby either,' Clementine said, 'so something definitely happened.'

'I think it's time to show this to the police.' Margery pointed to the diary. 'See what they think.'

'I agree,' Clementine said, though she did not look as though she entirely agreed. 'This is too much for us to deal with, isn't it? Let's hand it in tomorrow.'

Margery agreed.

–

'Gosh, Margery, I had such an amazing dream,' Margery heard Clementine say from the other side of the sagging air mattress. She could hear it hissing as the air deflated out of it while they lay on it in the tiny bedroom compartment of the tent. 'We won the lottery. Ooh, maybe it's a premonition. Quick, write the numbers down!'

'Please, Clem, it's much too early for lottery numbers,' Margery pleaded, pulling the sleeping bag over her face to block out Clementine's voice. The weather had indeed been as bad as they had thought and she had hardly slept a wink with the noise of the wind. That Clementine had managed to have a dream was slightly infuriating.

'Winning lottery numbers, you mean!' Clementine scoffed. 'Let me remember before the dream takes them. The numbers were…five…five…twenty-three and another two fives…oh no…wait…'

Margery pulled the covers from her head to smirk at her wife; Clementine rolled her eyes at her. 'Well, it was worth a go, wasn't it?'

Margery looked around the tent in dismay. The noise of the wind had died down and now they were left in an almost spooky near silence, the only noise the quiet hissing of the slowly deflating airbed.

'Should it not be a bit brighter in here, Clem?' she asked Clementine as she pointed to the clear plastic window at the top of the compartment door. 'I know it's an inside compartment, but surely that should have light coming through it. It's very…well, it's quite a luminous green in here, isn't it?' Clementine was right; the light in the tent was a very unnatural colour.

Clementine stood awkwardly, nearly tripping over the air bed as it sagged under her weight. 'I suppose so.'

She reached over and clumsily grasped for the zip at the bottom of the compartment opening, lifting it slowly. They were indeed greeted by the inside of the main tent, but not in the way that Margery had been expecting.

'Gosh,' Clementine said; she lunged forward and batted her arms against the tarpaulin. Margery fought against the sudden rush of claustrophobia that whirled up from her stomach. 'It's quite all right, Margery, the tent has just fallen down on top of us. Well, I hope that's what that is. You don't think it could be the sea do you?'

'Don't tell me you're still afraid of the sea,' Margery said. 'Not after we've been on a seaside holiday all week; it can't hurt you up here.'

'No, of course not. Well, maybe a bit. No one knows what's in it, do they? So many whales and bits of the *Titanic*.' Clementine chuckled nervously. 'Well, at least we've got plenty of air in here. Probably. Here, help me lift it up.'

Together they lifted the tarpaulin high enough to waddle out into the main compartment and prop it up again. Margery winced as her socks soaked instantly in the inch of water on the tent floor. The storm that had seemed to pass them by had poured in through the front of the tent as it had collapsed. The river of water had run through on one side – the side with all Margery's things, she noted with sadness as she picked up her wet towel from the top of her bag of clothes. It was all sopping wet. The books she had brought to enjoy of an evening were all ruined, the pages expanded in the water.

'Oh, look, fantastic news!' Clementine beamed at her from the other side of the tent. 'All my things are dry!'

She pulled dry cardigan after dry cardigan out of her suitcase, smiling, until she realised that Margery had not moved and was still clutching the waterlogged copy of the new Patricia Cornwall paperback.

'Oh, Margery. Your poor things.' Clementine rushed over and started to dab at Margery's suitcase with one of her dry socks.

Margery dropped the paperback, gasping. She scrabbled through her oversized beach bag, pulling out bits of soggy receipts and her special holiday towel that was soaking even though it had not yet even seen the sandy beach, until she found what she was looking for.

'Clem,' she moaned, 'the diary.' She held it up so Clementine could see it. It was destroyed, the pages fat and bulging out from the sleeve with water. She opened it and the ink had run horribly, turning the neat scrawl into a black and purple blob. Clementine stared for a long moment and then sat down heavily on the nearest bag, her head in her hands.

'I'm so sorry,' Margery breathed. She slumped down next to Clementine.

'It's okay,' Clementine finally said a moment later; she put her hand on Margery's shoulder and squeezed. Margery could see that she was very close to tears. It was unlike her, and she found a wave of worry washing over her as they sat in the tent, the water swishing around their bare feet and soaking the bottoms of their pyjamas. Clementine hesitated. Then she continued, 'I don't know, it's so silly. It's just that it was a little piece of someone else who might be…well…part of a family I never had, I suppose.'

'That doesn't sound silly at all,' Margery told her. Clementine sniffed, swiping at her eyes. 'I'd offer you a tissue, but they were all in my bag.' Clementine chuckled at that.

'Gosh, we should have taken our chances of getting murdered at Rose's house,' she said weakly.

Clementine's face fell again. 'So, what's the plan now?'

Chapter Eighteen

They did the only thing they could think to do and went to meet Dr Bell as he had requested. It was their only lead left, though Margery wasn't sure if it would take them anywhere. They had rung the police and told them about the diary and anything else they could think of. Detective Penfold took them seriously enough, taking any piece of new information as a gift. Margery assumed they were having no luck finding George and were desperate for anything that could help, but when they had told her the diary had been destroyed, she grew despondent, and the conversation ended soon after. Nevertheless, they had to see what Dr Bell wanted. They had no other avenues to pursue. She felt terrible about the diary, and she knew Clementine was still dreadfully upset about it, though she hadn't said anything more about it. She wished she'd brought it into the main compartment of the tent with her when they had gone to bed. She kept having that horrible sinking feeling she often got when she lost her favourite crochet hook.

They were sitting finishing a cream tea outside the small cafe on the cliffs, waiting for Dr Bell to join them. Upsettingly, the weather had improved so much that they no longer needed their raincoats, though they still carried them with them for posterity, and they could sit out on one of the picnic benches to the front of the building and enjoy the view. The sea was much calmer today, and there were even more surfers and swimmers making use of the waves.

'What do you think happened to Maria?' Clementine mused out loud for the hundredth time today. 'And that police officer that died?'

'No idea,' Margery sighed, getting her purse out of her handbag to pay the bill. Her hand brushed the wet diary as it left the bag and Margery found her thoughts wandering again.

'It's Dr Bell!' Clementine said, pointing over to the gate that led back up onto the footpath. He waved at them from the top of the hill. Clementine brushed the scone crumbs from her lap and grabbed her backpack. Margery left a ten-pound note on the table, safe from the wind, tucked under a cup, and they raced off towards him.

Dr Bell's was not too far away, but it could still be tricky to get to as the footpaths were worn and hard work. Margery felt glad she had remembered to put on sensible walking shoes this time but wished she had purchased one of the walking sticks she had seen when they had been planning their trip away. It would definitely be helpful right now. Neither she nor Clementine were prolific walkers, though, really. She knew once they got home that it would join the assortment of rarely used gardening equipment and Clementine's Argos catalogue collection in the shed. Her blisters from the other day were still bothering her and it made the walk even harder work. The trail took them up a steep hill, curving around the cliffs, and they had the most magnificent view of the sea below, tiny white lines of waves on the blue. The wind blew through Margery's hair pleasantly, offsetting the warmth from the late afternoon sun as they reached the man waiting for them at the top. He looked fully prepared for the walk with his sunglasses on and heavy hiking boots, the picture of health, parting the grass as he lumbered down towards them with big athletic strides.

'Hello!' he called over to them. 'Thank you for meeting me.'

'Why are we here?' Clementine demanded as they all continued walking up the footpath together. 'What on earth couldn't you have told us yesterday?'

'Or later, say, at a nice restaurant.' Margery asked.

Clementine snorted.

'Well, I must say that I was pleased when you arrived at my home, Clementine – is it Clementine, isn't it?' he asked. Clementine nodded. 'And you, Margery. I had been looking for you both.'

'Looking for us?' Margery asked nervously. They continued to stamp through the wiry grass of the path, across the hills and upwards.

'Yes,' he said firmly. 'I've been worried. Not just for me. But for you as well. None of this can be an accident. Someone planned to take me out and now they might try and take you out too. I must ask, has anything funny happened to you since?'

'Funnier than a man dying in front of us after being supposedly poisoned by someone who disappeared thirty-odd years ago?' Clementine's voice was laden with sarcasm, but Dr Bell just laughed.

'When you put it like that…my apologies. Bad choice of words.' They stopped at the stile and began to take it in turns to cross over the fence, Clementine first. 'I mean anything after that? I might be wrong, of course, but I just have a feeling this is still ongoing.'

'Lots of funny things, actually,' Clementine said. 'Some poisonous flowers left at the house we're staying at, and then our tyres were let down.'

Dr Bell didn't look surprised, which in turn surprised Margery. She wondered if he'd already suspected something was afoot for a while. He reached into his shoulder bag and pulled out a thermos flask.

'You don't know why someone would try and kill you?' Margery asked as Clementine helped her over the stile. Dr Bell held the plastic cup from the top of the thermos up in offering and then poured himself a cup when they both declined, their visit to the tearoom enough for the moment. He stowed the flask back in his bag.

'No.' He shook his head, the liquid from the flask billowing from the cup, great swathes of steam caught by the wind blowing across the field. 'Well, I suppose I was friends with Maria Glover, who everyone thought was the original poisoner...'

'But you never did?' Margery asked.

'Never.' He shook his head furiously and took the first step up onto the beginning of the fence, carefully manoeuvring so as to not spill his drink. 'Like I said earlier, we were good friends. She would have told me.'

'You were good friends?' Margery asked, still thinking immediately of Maria's diary. 'How good friends?'

Dr Bell had paused, sitting on the piece of fence that joined the two steps of the stile together and took a swig from the cup, scrunching his face at the taste of whatever was in it.

'Very good friends,' he said. 'Gosh, I thought the taste might have got better the second cup.' He swung his legs over and joined them in the field.

'Maria wouldn't have killed anyone,' he said adamantly, his blue eyes boring into Margery's own. 'It's all mad; she wouldn't have poisoned anyone. She knew her stuff – that's why the police thought she did it. She was a very good chef, her food was marvellous, but she would never have harmed anyone.'

'We know that,' Margery said, thinking of the last few entries of Maria's diary they had read. 'But if not her, then who? Someone's certainly poisoning people and we've suspected Emily from the hotel since we caught her foraging near here. But she can't have been the original poisoner; she would have been a baby at most back then.'

'Could Colin have been both?' Clementine asked suddenly. 'Could he still be the poisoner? I mean, that doesn't explain where Maria disappeared to. How did she escape?'

'Someone helped her escape, the only explanation.' Dr Bell downed the rest of his drink and began to walk again. 'I suspect George helped her; I thought it then and after his recent little disappearing act I'm sure he did.'

'But you don't think George is the poisoner?' Margery asked him. Everyone else seemed to, though they now suspected Emily above anyone else.

'He could well be; he knows a lot about the things that grow here. But then all of them do.' Dr Bell bounded along like he had been a mountain goat in a former life. Margery and Clementine struggled behind him. 'All the best foraging places in St Martin's are on Colin's land.'

'But George is the chef at the hotel, isn't he?' Clementine asked, out of breath in his wake.

'Well, no, not any more. George has particularly bad rheumatoid arthritis. Very bad indeed.' Dr Bell raised his hands, touching the knuckles on one with the fingers of the other. 'I prescribe what I can, but he can barely move his fingers most days. Last time I examined him he couldn't make a fist; he would struggle to hold a kitchen knife nowadays. I think Colin keeps him on out of principle. There's no way he's doing any of the gardening or cooking he's supposed to be. I'm sure he's roped Emily into doing most of it.'

Margery thought of the lumps she had noticed on George's knuckles when they had met him. If the doctor was being truthful, then there was no way George could have even lifted a pan, let alone worked an entire shift in a kitchen, even if the hotel was not particularly busy.

'So, who do you think killed Nathan, then?' Margery asked him. Clementine was deep in thought still, wandering along behind them. They reached the next fence and came to a stop.

'Well, I don't think it was Colin, if that's what you're asking. I know he's not very nice, but the fact of the matter is he's a businessman and a very successful one at that. There's no way he'd ever do anything to harm his business. No way. No, I think Emily was cooking that night and Colin is protecting her by blaming George, but I just can't see what her motive would be. No, I think something else is at play here.'

'What were you doing at the hotel that day? With Nathan and Andrea,' Margery asked. 'Do you eat there a lot?'

'No, not really,' he said. The fence wobbled a bit as he leaned on it for support. 'You've seen where I live; I like to keep myself to myself. But I was doing Emily a favour.'

'Emily?' Clementine said. 'What were you doing for Emily?'

'Helping her convince Colin to get treatment,' Dr Bell said.

'Treatment?' Clementine asked. 'For what?'

'No idea yet.' The doctor tried to smile but his eyes were glassy, his stare seemingly far away. 'Emily says he keeps having breathlessness and kidney pain. I prescribe him statins anyway, but I'd like to give him a proper check-up; he hasn't had one for a long while and he keeps avoiding it whenever I try to corner him. She told me he hasn't been well for some time now.'

They reached the end of the field and came to a stop before the next stile, but the doctor didn't make any attempt to climb over. His eyes were still glazed over; his skin was clammy.

'Are you all right, Doctor?' Clementine asked. 'Aren't we going to carry on... Where were we going?'

Dr Bell looked down at the cup still in his hand and groaned.

'The tea...' he wheezed, 'Emily...'

'Tea? Emily...what?' Margery asked in alarm. He dropped the cup to the ground, where it rolled away from them through the grass and grasped at his chest, the wheezing becoming worse and worse. His lungs sounded like they were filling rapidly with cement as he gasped for breath and clutched at his own chest.

'Poison!' he managed to splutter out, before crumpling to the ground.

Chapter Nineteen

Once Dr Bell was in the ambulance, they had staggered back up onto the main road and rung the police, Clementine babbling madly that the doctor had been poisoned by Emily. Detective Penfold had met them as they wandered aimlessly up the road, still in shock, and picked them up in the police car. She drove much faster than either Margery or Clementine had ever dreamed of, swinging around the corners of the country lanes, the car bouncing over potholes, and ignoring traffic signs.

'It'll be all right, Margery,' Clementine whispered, taking her hand, and Margery clung on to the car seat with the other. 'They'll catch her, and this will all be over.'

Margery was not so sure it would. For one thing, why would Emily poison Dr Bell when she wanted his help? She had seen the surprise in his eyes as he lay on the ground clutching his chest through his shirt. His pale, surprised faced kept bouncing back into her mind and she kept batting it away again. She remembered the tea on his kitchen table with the sticker attached and wondered if that was the batch that had poisoned him.

Margery found her mind wandering to Ceri-Ann. Gloria had texted the night before to say that they were back at Rose's and all was all right for now, but Margery couldn't help worrying still. It seemed everyone in the small village had a secret to hide. Everyone except her and Clementine. She wondered very briefly if Clementine had ever known she might have a younger sister out in the world, but she knew Clementine well enough to know that she could not keep a secret to save her life. Margery had spent years having her birthday and Christmas presents spoiled by Clementine blurting them out by accident. Another ambulance screamed past them, going the opposite way, the sirens wailing as it pulled up alongside them for a moment before disappearing. Margery and Clementine gasped in surprise.

'What's happening?' Clementine breathed from beside her. Margery did not know.

Detective Penfold eyed her in the rear-view mirror, her eyes piercing into theirs like a hawk. It had been foolish to get themselves wrapped up in all of this with no defences at all, Margery thought. Just a couple of middle-aged dinner ladies nearly getting themselves killed, for the second or third time now. She thought back to the look on Dr Bell's face in the field. He had been very calm before, and not at all on guard or expecting to be poisoned.

They came to a stop outside Merrowpool police station. Margery tried instinctively to leave the vehicle but was trapped inside by the child locks until Detective Penfold let them both out. It was only when they were sitting back down in the tiny interview room that Margery began to process any of what had happened. They gave their statement, explaining what had happened to the doctor out in the field and what they had seen – how Dr Bell had collapsed after telling them Emily had poisoned him; how they had seen some of Emily's tea at his house. Detective Penfold noted it all down.

'One more thing before you go,' she said. Margery had had enough for one day. All she wanted to do was go back to Rose's and find somewhere to lie down and sleep it off. 'Where is George Kale?'

'No idea,' Clementine said, the anger clear in her voice. Margery shook her head too. Surely if the police did not know where George was, then they would have no chance of knowing. She wished they did know; she was sure he could help them. Detective Penfold hummed as though she did not believe them, playing with the pen on the table in front of her.

'Why are you here?' Clementine retorted. 'Everyone keeps saying how you've been working in Plymouth. Why are you back in Merrowpool now, for this? Just to pick on a couple of older ladies who had nothing to do with any of—'

'The police officer who died the night Maria Glover disappeared was my uncle,' Detective Penfold snapped, cutting Clementine off mid-sentence. 'That's why!'

'What…?' Margery began, but she realised mid-word that it made perfect sense. Of course she would have returned to avenge him as soon as she had found out about the new poisoning. She stared at the detective's face; she must be under an incredible amount of strain to have snapped at them like that.

'What happened to him?' Clementine asked. 'No one seems to know.'

'No one knows, not for sure anyway,' Detective Penfold said. Her voice was much calmer; she had regained control of it in the few seconds since her outburst. 'My uncle was the officer in charge of Maria Glover's case. He made the initial arrest.'

Margery and Clementine listened quietly.

'The next morning, after they'd had her in custody for the night, a batch of elderflower cordial was sent to the station with a thank-you note for catching the poisoner. There was a name with it, but it was fake. They all thought they were being thanked by someone in the village for a job well done,' Detective Penfold explained. 'They all had a celebration drink—'

'That seems stupid,' Margery said before she could stop herself. Detective Penfold gestured in a way that told Margery she thought it was very stupid too.

'Yes, everyone except my uncle had a little glass.'

'It was poisoned?' Clementine guessed.

'Sleeping pills, absolutely laced with them. They tested it later and it would have killed a child probably.' The detective shook her head. 'I've seen the case file. All those officers were lucky to keep their jobs after. A stupid thing to do.'

'So, the poisoner?' Margery said; she didn't want to press her for the story but she couldn't stop herself. She remembered one of the first entries of Maria's diary she had read, where Maria had wondered if her elderflower wine was ready. Maybe she had made the drink for the officers herself.

'What happened after that is a bit hazy,' she said. 'At the time, Merrowpool station had one CCTV camera and it was just inside the main entrance.'

'Just the one?' Margery asked in shock.

'Back then Merrowpool wasn't the bustling metropolis you see today,' Penfold said sarcastically. 'The most trouble you got then, and now to be honest, was the odd drunk making an idiot of themselves.' The pen rolled away from her fingertips across the table and Margery caught it, handing it back to her. She took the pen at the same time as she took a deep breath, preparing herself to continue. 'They had footage of someone going in, face covered, all planned, you know? And then the same person running out with Maria, my uncle following shortly behind them and then all we know after...' She inhaled again. 'All we know after is that he washed up on the beach days later. His squad car was found at the hotel.'

'They went back there,' Margery said, 'but why?'

'Exactly,' Penfold said. 'So, you can see why we thought you were suspicious.' She nodded at Clementine. 'Turning up looking like her and then another poisoning. We thought you might be a relative. They never IDed who helped her escape.'

Margery thought about Penfold's uncle; had he known who Maria's mystery helper was? She wondered how he had known to go to the hotel otherwise, and why would Maria go back there?

'And this time Colin told you George was cooking?' Clementine said. Penfold nodded. 'Did you suspect him anyway?' She nodded again.

'I suspect someone from the hotel helped them from there. Maria has never been found, body or otherwise.'

'Dr Bell said George couldn't have been working in the kitchen that night Nathan died,' Margery finally said. 'Because of his arthritis. He can barely move his hands.'

Detective Penfold looked at her with great interest at that. 'Really?' she said. 'What else did he tell you?'

'Not much,' Clementine said, fiddling with the buttons of her cardigan. 'We didn't get much more time to speak before...well.'

There was a rap on the door; all three of them turned to watch as the male officer who had taken their statement at the hotel on the night Nathan died entered the room.

He gestured for Detective Penfold and she got up and went to him. Outside the room, their voices were low, muttering, and Margery had to strain her ears. Even then she couldn't hear a single syllable of it. She watched as Penfold's mouth dropped open; whatever he'd told her must have been deadly serious.

–

Rose was waiting for them in one of the hard waiting-room chairs in the reception of the station. She looked up as they arrived and rose to her feet. Christopher stood too and brushed the creases from his trousers, grabbing his green waxed coat from the back of the chair. Even with Rose wearing her heels, he still towered over her.

'Hello,' Margery said, her voice feeling weak after hours of denying accusations.

'I've been here making a statement about yesterday,' Rose said sadly. She looked awfully tired. 'Thought I'd stay and wait for you after that mad message Clem texted me. I can't believe someone tried to kill Dr Bell. It's just not the way things are done, is it?'

'No,' Margery said weakly, not quite sure if she had the brainpower to deal with an enraged drama teacher at that moment. Rose continued, oblivious.

'And the tent collapsing like that! Just awful. I'm going to go to down to the erection section and give them a piece of my mind! Come on, let's get out of here before they arrest you again for loitering.' She gave the innocent receptionist on the desk a glare before sash-aying out through the main doors. Margery thought about weakly protesting that they hadn't been arrested at all but didn't have the energy. Instead they followed her and

Christopher outside, him holding the doors for them all and looking between them apologetically.

'Did they find out who was at your house?' Margery said dazedly, her voice feeling very far away.

'No.' Rose glowered, but she took Christopher's arm in hers. 'Thank God Christopher's been around to support me. James is still in France. He's coming back tonight; I told him to stay and enjoy his stag, but he can't bear to after all this nonsense.'

The drive back to the house was much the same. Rose babbled on about how excited she was that the head-master was coming home, and how they must return to her house now the tent was practically destroyed. It filled the silence in the car nicely as Margery and Clementine both processed Dr Bell's collapse and the loss of Maria's diary. Through their gloom, however, Margery noticed that Christopher did not join in on Rose's joy at James Barrow's impending arrival. He looked rather stony-faced in the front passenger seat, as though he could not think of a single thing in the world worse. There was some-thing familiar about his coat, Margery thought to herself, but she was quickly distracted as Rose pulled into her driveway.

Rose and Christopher got out and began to walk over to the house. As she was gathering her things, Clem-entine's phone rang, making Margery jump. The worst thing about Clementine's ringtone was that it was the same as her alarm and Margery had developed a horrible Pavlovian response to it. Clementine rattled around in her bag until she found it and answered with a gruff 'Hello', her eyes widening as she listened to the voice on the end of the line.

'It's Sophie,' she hissed. She jabbed at her phone until she managed to put it on speaker. Sophie's voice rang out, unnaturally high in pitch and out of breath.

'…and then I spoke to Nan but she didn't know what was going on and—'

'Slow down, Sophie,' Clementine said. 'Are you all right? What's happened?'

'They arrested Emily from the hotel, Mr Warrell's girlfriend!' Sophie's voice shouted over the phone line. 'I had to let you know! Looks like you're going to be off the hook.'

'They arrested her?' Margery said.

'She poisoned Mr Warrell too! And the mayor, they think!'

'What!' Margery and Clementine cried in unison.

'I know! Her own fiancé! He's in hospital!' Sophie sounded much too excited, Margery thought. She was probably thinking of the article headline already.

'But how?' Clementine demanded.

'She poisoned him with monkshood. Basically, they thought he was having a heart attack but Thomas told the police that he'd seen Emily making him a tea just before and he thought there was something wrong with it. He's so upset. He thought his dad was going to die!'

'But…how did they know what it was?' Margery asked, confused.

'Thomas told them he recognised the plant,' Sophie said. 'He's quite a keen gardener himself, actually, and he helps Emily out a lot foraging. He just a bit embarrassed about it all, doesn't think it's cool. Anyway, monkshood is really poisonous! You can die if you even get it on your skin.'

'We've just been with Dr Bell. He's been taken to hospital after being poisoned,' Clementine said, her voice very small. 'What if he was drinking tea with monkshood in too? What if he dies?'

'I...I don't know.' Sophie sounded less excited now. More like she had realised how terrible this all was. The conversation rattled off and they said their goodbyes.

'Poisoned,' Margery breathed.

'Looks like Emily's been the new poisoner all along, then,' Clementine said, still staring at the phone.

'Well, she couldn't have been the original, could she? Much too young, like we've already thought,' Margery said. She watched through the car window as Christopher lingered outside, smoking.

'So Emily must have prepared the food the night the mayor died; why else would Colin cover for her? He told the police he suspected Maria, didn't he? She wrote that in her diary.'

'That's true.' Margery couldn't stop watching Christopher. There was something of note about him tonight, something important that would stitch together a mystery, but she couldn't put her finger on what it was.

'God, everyone's strange here, aren't they?' Clementine rubbed her eyes before she put her glasses back on. The humour was back in her voice, Margery noticed; it had been gone since they had accidentally drowned Maria's diary.

'They're all strange back home too,' Margery reminded her. 'Remember when Mr Fitzgerald kept calling global warming "the greenhouse ceiling"?'

Clementine laughed and so did she, and for a moment she could try and forget all the terrible things that had happened over the last few days. Eventually, they both fell silent, and she took Clementine's hand and kissed it.

'So...' Clementine leaned over and rested her head on Margery's shoulder. 'What's next? Emily might well have been arrested, but where's George gone? Why did he run off if he's innocent?'

Margery thought about it for a few minutes, finally able to think again in the peace and silence of the car. She wondered if they should try and contact the mayor's wife and warn her, but she assumed the police would probably already be on that. Detective Penfold didn't seem to be the type of person to let anything be left to chance.

'Do you know who might know a bit more about what happened originally?' she finally said. 'Prue. She's been in the village for decades, and she knows everyone. She might know who Maria was talking about in her diary.'

'And she was in that picture at the hotel in the flat, wasn't she?' Clementine hummed. 'I think you might be on to something there!'

'Yes, she might be able to tell us more about Janice too,' Margery said.

'You don't think Janice...?'

'I do, I think she had something to do with all this. I just don't know what yet.'

'Why?' Clementine asked. 'Just because of the diary entries?'

Margery thought back to Janice's house, of the water-colour paintings of plants. Of the gardening books on the bookcase. It couldn't hurt to talk to her neighbour.

Chapter Twenty

Margery and Clementine had slept in the comfortable bed at Rose's again but had seen no need in waiting around the next morning after listening to her flap around them all night. They had barely stayed for a bit of breakfast before rushing off in the car to the village. It had taken so long to find somewhere to park that it was nearly half past ten when they were furiously knocking on Prue's front door. They waited. Margery was convinced this was the right place to come. She just had a hunch that there were answers here. She wanted to know what her relation was to everyone else. Had she worked for Colin? Was she another of Maria's kitchen assistants, like Janice? Which stupid nickname had Maria given her in the diary?

'Hello!' came a tiny voice. It made Margery and Clementine both flinch.

'Hello!' it came again. Margery looked to the left of the house and saw the elderly woman gazing up at them from her living room window again, as she had when they had visited the first time.

'Hello, Prue,' Margery said. Prue beamed at them.

'I thought it was you!' Prue said gleefully. 'Are you seeing Janice again?'

'Actually,' Clementine said, 'we came to chat with you. Is that okay?'

'Is that okay?' Prue scoffed. She disappeared from the window for a moment and then the front door popped open. Prue stood in the doorway, beaming from ear to ear.

They both followed her in through the front door and into the house. It was just as stuffed with items as Janice's house had been. Prue had obviously lived here for just as long a time – the cabinets were jammed full of trinkets collected over years, all covered in an inch of dust – and yet in a way it seemed much tidier than Janice's household. Everything was just a bit more organised. Prue led them through the living room, and out across the small kitchen into her back garden. It was not a traditional garden layout. For one it was long and narrow and on different levels, very much like the garden Margery had seen through the window of the Hornbottom residence. The bottom level by the kitchen door was a small courtyard surrounded by tall walls, which Prue obviously spent most of her time weeding. Then, leading up out of the courtyard over the wall and onto the next layer of the garden was a set of steep and precarious stone stairs, with a bistro dining set on the terrace above. It all looked quite unsafe to Margery's eyes; there was not even a hint of a banister or any such handhold. She was sure it would fail a risk assessment if it were part of her kitchen at work.

'Go on, go on!' Prue gestured at them, her hands and arms flailing wildly at the stairs. 'I'll make the tea!'

'Can we help?' Margery asked. Prue shooed her away.

'I never get guests!' She smiled. 'Let me enjoy it!'

Margery and Clementine shared a look, before Clementine readied herself and began to climb the staircase. Margery followed begrudgingly. She chose her steps carefully and took them slowly. Soon enough they were up at the top of the garden and sitting on the garden chairs under the shade of the apple trees, the fruit on them beginning to ripen. The breeze blowing through the leaves was cool and calming.

'Well,' Margery said, looking around at the well-kept garden. 'This is nice.'

'It's lovely,' Clementine replied. Though she looked sullen, as though she were mulling a lot over in her mind. The usual Clementine that had returned last night had disappeared again and Margery was worried that she would never be quite the same.

'What's wrong?' Margery asked her.

'It's just… I just feel like we're giving up, like we haven't finished what we started,' Clementine said. 'I don't know if this is going to help at all.'

'You're the queen of not finishing anything you start,' Margery reminded her. 'Remember that cookbook you were going to write when you had gallstones – the guide on what you could and couldn't eat? Ooh, what were you going to call it?'

'*Unmitigated Gall*,' Clementine said.

'That's it!' Margery smiled at her. 'You never finished writing that. You wrote two recipes, if I remember.'

'Yes, but all I really fancied eating when I was ill was jam on toast,' Clementine said sadly. 'There's only so many ways you can write that down, Margery.'

Margery hummed agreeably. She had a pretty good view over and into Janice and Sophie's garden from her seat. The gardens were not private in any way, shape or form. Janice's was a bit tidier that Prue's but not as well weeded. The Hornbottom courtyard was full of potted plants and herbs and had bunting running up and down the bit of fence that Margery could see. They looked over most of the house from here too. Prue could probably peer right into one of the bedrooms from here if she wanted, seeing as the French doors of one of them opened out onto the weird staired garden.

Prue wobbled up the stairs precariously, balancing a tea tray. Clementine jumped up to help her, but she shooed her away, kicking her feet at her to keep her back.

'Here we are, ladies!' she said triumphantly as she made it to the top of the staircase without falling backward and dying horribly. 'Tea for three! Oh no.' She squinted at the tea tray in her hands. 'I forgot the teapot!'

She turned and began to wobble back down. Clementine once again went to help her but without Prue's agreement the most she could do was watch her totter her way back down hopelessly. Margery found her eyes being drawn to the first-floor window of Janice's house again. The bedroom doors were open a tad; the long curtains on either side of the doorway were blowing gently in the morning breeze. Prue finally made it back up with the teapot and sat down with them. She handed them each a plate and they all tucked in.

'This jam is lovely,' Margery said as she ate the scone Prue had presented her with.

'It's Janice's hedgerow jam.' Prue grinned. 'I don't know how she makes it so good, but she goes out and picks all the berries for it herself. She used to do a lot of that, but she stopped for a bit, you know?'

'We wanted to ask if you knew anything about that – foraging and the poisoner...and Janice,' Margery said, deciding that if they were going to ask then they should just get on with it. They had wasted enough time as it was. They hadn't even managed to get Rose's hen party shopping yet; the hours left of the week were whittling away to nothing, evaporating like early morning dew. Soon they would have to leave St Martin's and go back to Dewstow, back to work at the school. Back to normality, although Margery couldn't say she would miss the village at all. Prue's gentle joviality had been replaced by a calm sort of acceptance, as though she had known the real reason for their visit the entire time.

'Ask away,' she said, stirring her teacup with the ornate teaspoon. 'Ask away.'

'I don't know how much you've heard about the recent poisonings—' Margery began.

Prue interrupted her. 'I know everything.'

'Everything?' Margery whispered.

'Everything!' Prue nodded, taking a sip of tea. 'So, ask me.'

'You worked at the hotel?' Margery asked. 'In the kitchen?'

'No!' Prue scoffed as though the idea was simply ridiculous. 'I was a cleaner. I was there for ages – had to retire in the end, though, a few years ago. Too much work for me.'

'But you knew Maria?' Margery asked.

'Of course! She used to call me Scrubs.' Prue burst into laughter at the memory. 'Always joking around.'

'Like in the diary,' Margery gasped. 'Do you know who Artie is? Or Bubbles?'

Prue considered it as she ate her scone. 'Bubbles is probably a kitchen porter they had for a bit, can't remember the name… He put washing-up liquid in the dishwasher by mistake and it bubbled up everywhere.' She chuckled. Her brow furrowed. 'Artie? Not sure about that one. I never heard her call someone that, and I personally don't remember anyone.'

'Why has George disappeared if he didn't have anything to do with the poisoning?' Clementine blurted out. Prue did not look shocked at all.

'Of course he didn't have anything to do with that.' Prue laughed again. 'George hasn't worked in that kitchen for years! That's that awful Colin Warrell for you, always hiding things.'

'He doesn't own your house too, does he?' Margery asked, suddenly concerned that Colin was holding Prue's roof over her head too.

'No, but I might be better off if he did!' Prue laughed again, but she didn't feel it necessary to let Margery or Clementine in on the joke. 'Janice barely pays him anything now.'

'But Janice said…'

'I know what she tells people, but he's not all bad,' Prue said. 'The only reason he never sold it back to her is because of what she did.'

'What did she do?' Margery asked, hoping her voice didn't sound as shocked as she felt.

'What didn't she do? Nasty piece of work, Janice – I worked with her for years! Always the same.' Prue tutted and poured them all another cup of tea, though Margery had barely touched hers; the liquid filled the delicate china cup right to the brim. 'The police have already been round asking if I know where he is,' she continued, 'but I didn't tell them a thing. You're different, though, you can tell.'

'Can you?' Clementine asked. 'Well, I suppose we aren't wearing police uniforms.'

Prue guffawed, throwing her head back with the force of it. 'No, and they think he had something to do with that hotel, though I don't know if they still believe that now. Such nonsense, all of it.'

'Do you know where he is?' Margery asked.

'Of course,' Prue said.

They considered each other. Prue took another sip from her cup and Margery wondered if she would ever tell them. Instead, she took a piece of folded paper out of her pocket and reached out for Margery's hand, placing it on her palm and then folding her fingers closed.

'The address. I knew you'd come and ask for it eventually,' Prue whispered. Margery opened her hand to look at the paper and almost gasped in surprise.

'You can't be serious?' Margery looked up from the paper to Prue. 'He's been at the campsite this entire time? How hasn't anyone seen him?'

'I take him food,' Prue said proudly. 'He's okay; I check on him every other day.'

Prue helped herself to a scone and took a bite. Margery watched the jam slide off it onto the plate, gooey and gloopy in the mid-morning light. She found her eyes drawn to the pearlescent buttons of Prue's cardigan, glinting in the sunlight.

Margery was surprised by Clementine's gasp next to her. She stood quickly and grasped Margery's arm for support.

'Janice!' she hissed, her eyes boggling at the open bedroom door in the next garden.

'What?' Margery said dumbly, still holding the paper in her fist.

'Janice,' Clementine whispered. 'Look at the window. She's collapsed on the floor by the bed!'

'By the bed?' Margery breathed, standing to look where Clementine was looking. Sure enough, through the open bedroom doors there was a body lying on the floor, their grey hair only just visible. 'Oh, I can see her.'

Prue had stood too, wobbling on her feet for a moment before grabbing the table to steady herself. 'I can see her too.'

'Oh, Clem, we've got to get in there!' Margery cried.

Clementine looked around wildly; she rushed to the fence and looked over the boundary into Janice's garden. Before Margery or Prue could stop her, she was swinging a leg over the fence and clambering over into the other side. She landed with a thump on the grass as gracefully as Seren making an omelette first thing on a Monday morning at work.

'Come on, Margery!' she said, rushing across Janice's garden with as much ease as her old legs would manage and entering Janice's bedroom. Margery could see her kneeling down on the floor next to the woman. Margery made to follow her, but she was wearing a long summer skirt and could not work out how she could manage it without tearing it. Prue stood by the table still, wringing her hands.

'Let me in through the front door, Clem!' she shouted as loudly as she could to Clementine and then she rushed to the steps on Prue's side of the garden.

'Call an ambulance, Prue!' Margery called as she carefully manoeuvred down the steep stone stairs. 'We'll come for tea another time!'

'Wait!' Prue wailed after her, standing frozen to the spot, her eyes as wide as the saucers on the table. Margery didn't wait for her to follow. She rushed through Prue's house and out the front door, nearly colliding with Clementine in the doorway as she unlocked Janice's door from the inside.

'Oh, Margery, this is bad, very, very bad!' Clementine moaned. 'We need to call an ambulance. You go and try and get her ready and I'll ring on my phone and then wait outside for them.' She fumbled her mobile phone from the pocket of her shorts with shaky hands and dialled 999.

'I asked Prue to call, but I think she's in shock. Where is she?'

'Main bedroom.' Clementine was sweaty and out of breath. She had a wild look of panic in her eyes that Margery had not seen since they had almost been killed last year. Margery braced herself for the worst and entered the house.

The living room looked much the same as it had the other day, with the notable absence of either Janice or Sophie. She glanced around for a moment before heading up the stairs, huffing and puffing as she went.

'Janice?' she asked gingerly as she pushed open the bedroom door. Janice was lying by the bed in the same position Margery had seen her in from the garden. 'Clementine's calling an ambulance.'

'Oh good,' Janice said from where she was slumped against the bed. She winced, sucking the air through her teeth as she tried to sit up. There was a spark there, still in her eyes, but it was so faint that Margery thought that it could go out at any moment. 'Probably won't help, though.'

'What do you mean?' Margery helped her sit up. Janice groaned and clutched at her sides.

'Been poisoned,' Janice said wheezily. Margery noticed the tea mug on the floor next to her on its side; it had spilled all over the rug in front of the bed where Janice had obviously dropped it. 'They won't get here in time.'

'Of course they will.' Margery tried to sound encouraging but her voice failed her. She thought about the watercolour paintings and the hedgerow jam and suddenly realised that Janice probably knew a lot more about plants and poisons than she let on. 'Won't they?'

'Maybe,' Janice said agreeably. She did not look very well. Her pupils were huge, and her hands were trembling as she clutched the duvet cover beneath her. She must have slid from the bed and dragged it down onto the floor with her as she went.

'How do you know? Are you sure?' Margery asked. 'Poisoned with what?'

'Hemlock, of course.' Janice struggled the words out thickly. 'It's hemlock. I should have known. Grows all over the place here.'

'Was it the tea?' Margery asked, gesturing to the cup on the floor. Janice nodded, seemingly unable to speak. 'Where did you get it from? Is it one of Emily's?'

'It was a gift,' Janice rasped out.

'From who?'

'It was sent to Sophie at the paper.' Her eyes were going in and out of focus. Margery suddenly remembered the tea canister she had seen on the kitchen counter downstairs when they had been here last. It looked so much like the ones Emily had made at the hotel, and that Dr Bell had in his kitchen. Maybe they were one and the same. Had Emily sent it to Sophie to kill her like she had tried to kill Colin and Dr Bell? She couldn't make sense of why she would have done that, or why she had poisoned the doctor. Why Sophie of all people?

'We'll call the police too, then,' Margery told her. She meant it as comfort, but Janice opened her eyes even wider and clawed desperately at Margery's hand.

'No. No police!'

'Janice…' Margery asked, already fearing the answer, her brain flickering to the mentions of her in Maria's diary. Prue's obvious distaste for her. 'How do you know so much about poisons?'

Janice did not reply for a moment. Her body was so still that Margery began to think the worst had happened, but then she took a big, gasping breath and clutched Margery's hand. 'I…' she rasped. 'I was the poisoner.'

Chapter Twenty-One

Detective Penfold had not even pretended to be surprised to see them when they had given their statement at Treliske hospital. Janice had already been rushed there by ambulance and they had called Sophie as they followed it in the car. Margery had felt strangely calm when she and Clementine had been sitting down in the safety of the A&E ward, but now they were on the move again, she felt the panic arrive. She didn't know if they ought to have told Detective Penfold that they knew where George was. Clementine had argued that they needed to know for certain what his involvement was before they did, and besides it looked like he would walk free regardless now that Emily had been pinned for everything. Clementine was convinced that the whole thing was too simple, but she couldn't explain why she thought that. Even when Detective Penfold had told them that it looked like Colin had been being poisoned over a long period, this time being the one that had nearly killed him.

'It's just too simple.' Clementine shook her head as they drove along. 'Okay, maybe she had a reason for poisoning Colin, but why Janice? How did she even know her? What's her motive? And Dr Bell? Why try to kill him? Also, did we actually see Emily that day on the fields?'

'Of course we did,' Margery said, but she suddenly realised that they hadn't seen her face at all. 'She was wearing that purple coat.'

'Anyone could have been wearing it,' Clementine explained. 'Her face was covered.'

'Well, if she was picking some nasty stuff she'd have covered her hands and eyes, wouldn't she? She wouldn't want to risk any of it touching her skin. If not Emily, then who are you suggesting it was? There seems to be overwhelming evidence against her.'

'Someone who wanted to frame her for it, get her out of the picture,' Clementine said.

Margery thought about it for a second. 'Could Janice be the only poisoner? She obviously hates Colin for historical reasons, doesn't she? What if it is still her?'

'And kill herself or her own grandchild? No. You heard her before: family is everything.' Clementine tilted her head to the side as though pouring all the thoughts into that part of her brain. 'How did Thomas know what the plant was? Why didn't he stop her if he saw her chopping it up?'

'Y-you think Thomas poisoned his dad? And the doctor and Janice?' Margery spluttered incredulously, thinking about Sophie's phone call and Emily's arrest; it almost made her stall the car as they took a particularly steep road. 'Why?'

'Well, I don't think Janice, the original poisoner, would poison herself enough to kill herself and this new poisoner obviously knows their way around deadly substances too, don't they?' Clementine seemed to have made up her mind. 'Just because all those teas were similar to the ones Emily makes doesn't mean she isn't being framed.'

They reached their destination. Margery hadn't needed to put the postcode into the maps feature on her phone; she had known exactly where to go. It seemed darkly amusing that George had been so close the entire time and their next obvious point of interest after the conversation with Colin Warrell. They had even walked there the day before, had left the car at Rose's and rushed down the footpath to their tent. It was late afternoon by the time they arrived at the campsite and much, much brighter than it had been the day before when the tent had subsided under the weight of the rain. It was practically the Sahara now in comparison; the wind had dropped off completely and left only bright afternoon sunshine.

They moved through at a fast pace, leaving the car parked outside the reception. Past the play area full of children screaming happily, past the tents and caravans of families in shorts and T-shirts setting up barbecues and deckchairs, and past Rose's tent, which they had left there lying wonkily the day before. Until they reached the far-right corner of the campsite. Barely noticeable in the very corner pitch, hidden by bushes, was a small green tent, the kind that was called 'two-man' but really meant 'one person and maybe a bag'. Margery wondered for a moment what proper tent etiquette was and whether she should try and knock somehow but before she had finished the thought, Clementine had reached down and unzipped the tent.

'Hello?' she called inside. 'Is that you, George?'

They stepped back and waited for a moment. The tent remained still.

'We know it's you, George,' Margery said, shaking the front tent pole. It rattled the canvas in a satisfying way, so she did it again and again. Clementine joined her.

'Okay, okay!' George crawled out of the unzipped door and climbed out awkwardly with his arms over his head. He had been asleep, his pyjamas looking oddly out of place among the holiday-goers in summer clothes and sunglasses. The tent was so stuffed full of his belongings, it bulged at the sides, the suitcases either side of the sad-looking foam mattress he had been lying on. 'You've got me! Arrest me if you must.'

He looked around and seemed startled to see both of them, slowly lowering his hands. 'You're not the police.'

Margery knew he was going to run before he even moved – she could tell by the way his eyes shifted as he looked behind them both – but she was not fast enough to stop him. She reached out for the back of his pyjama top as he rushed past them, nearly bowling them over in his hurry to escape. They chased after him, apologising to families as he jumped over tent guy ropes and pushed people out of the way.

'You've got to leave me and get after him, Margery,' Clementine wheezed, determination flaring in her eyes as they reached the halfway point between George's tent pitch and the campsite reception. 'I'll never catch him with my asthma.'

Margery nodded, and she began to pick up speed racing after George, Clementine just steps behind her. She rushed into the campsite car park and nearly ran straight in front of a passing car. They beeped the horn at her, but she kept going. She could see George frantically looking for somewhere to hide behind the parked-up burger van, the staff inside staring at him curiously.

He pulled a bag of burger buns from its home on the van's countertop and flung it in their direction, forcing Margery and Clementine to scatter as it careened towards them, the man it belonged to shrieking 'Oi!' as they whipped past him. Clementine was struggling to keep up and Margery took the lead in the pursuit as she had suggested. She was giving up hope of catching him as he sprinted across the car park and veered around the corner, her legs stiff and her lungs burning with the effort. She made it around the corner of the reception building, abandoning Clementine to take her asthma inhaler, just in time to watch George trip over a loose paving stone and stumble to the floor, groaning in pain as he caught his fall with his hands. He dragged himself up from the ground at the bottom of a set of concrete stairs that led to what looked like a staff smoking area.

'Are you okay?' she panted, trying to catch her breath.

'I think so,' he moaned as he got to his feet, brushing himself off. 'Why are you chasing me?'

'Well, why did you run?' Margery said.

'I don't know.' He put his head in his hands.

Clementine finally appeared around the corner and pointed at George dramatically.

'Stop that man!' she cried. George slumped down heavily on the first stair, the picture of defeat.

'You got me, you got me,' he gasped, wiping his face with a handkerchief.

'We know you didn't poison Nathan,' Margery said. George's face relaxed, the tension going out of it immediately.

'No, I did not.'

'Who was cooking the night Nathan died?' Margery demanded to know. She saw no reason for pleasantries, not now that she knew George could spring up and run off again like a terrified rabbit at any moment. 'Colin is insisting it was you, but we know it couldn't have been because of your hands.'

George held them up to show them how they were rigidly bent out of shape, his fingers angled off to one side. It looked extremely painful. 'Indeed, but the police were suspicious enough of me the first time and they definitely suspect me this time. Lord knows that was enough trouble and Colin will have changed the rota to say that I was on shift.' George looked absolutely miserable.

'He'd throw you under the bus?' Margery asked.

'Of course.' George nodded. 'He may have kept me around all these years, but that's because I know too much.'

'About what?'

'Lots of things.' He smiled, though it did not reach his eyes. 'His dealings at the hotel, the rental properties, Thomas's real father.'

'Thomas's real father?' Margery asked incredulously at the same time as Clementine cried, 'What?'

'Yes.' He nodded, exhaling deeply as though it were a weight from his chest to talk to someone about it. 'Do you know Arthur Bell? The doctor?'

'Yes?'

'Well, then, you've met Thomas's father.'

'Artie,' Margery gasped. She suddenly felt very tired. 'Maria had an affair?'

George hummed agreeably. 'She did. Well…Arthur had an affair to begin with. I'm assuming that Colin and Maria didn't really hit it off until much later, though I don't think she ever ended it. I think it only stopped when she disappeared. Colin knew about it all. He really did love her but I don't think she ever really felt the same way. He begged her to marry him once she found out she was pregnant, and she eventually agreed to.'

'We read her diary.' Clementine slumped down on the stairs next to him, looking as tired as Margery felt. 'We found it in your home.'

'Did you?' George chuckled; he didn't look angry at all. Quite the opposite. 'You must really be detectives! So, you know what happened?'

'Yes,' Margery breathed. Clementine nodded next to her. George looked down at his hands. For a moment Margery wasn't sure that he would tell them anything more, then he sighed deeply, his shoulders sinking back again.

'She ran, left the baby. She thought she had no choice, and she didn't really. She was going to prison,' he said. 'Colin called the police on her. He says he did it because he knew she was the poisoner, but I think it was because he'd found out that she was going to leave him for the doctor. Get him put on the birth certificate. Janice let it slip, you see, though I don't think that was an accident.'

'Where did she go?' Margery asked; she was confused by this part, as in the diary Maria seemed to have every intention of taking Thomas with her. 'And how on earth did she escape?'

'I don't know exactly what happened. It was late at night, and Maria and Janice turned up at my caravan outside the hotel and demanded I help her get out. The police at the station were all being violently ill, and Janice had used that as an opportunity to free Maria and get her back home. She'd just waltzed in there while everyone was being sick and released her from the holding cell! Can you imagine?'

It all matched up with Penfold's story, Margery thought grimly.

George smiled weakly. 'I thought you might work it all out. Poor Maria.' He gasped, looking as though he may burst into tears at any moment. 'She didn't deserve any of it.'

'So, Janice poisoned the police...' Margery tried to fit this new piece of information with the others in her mind. 'Why?'

'Guilt. She wanted to get back at Colin for buying her house. I told her she should have just sold it and bought somewhere cheaper but she wouldn't; I even offered for her to bunk with me for a bit but...' George trailed off, the memories obviously hard work to repeat. 'I think it was guilt. I've always felt that she felt bad for Maria taking the blame for it all, and I don't think she really meant for anyone to die, so she helped her get out.'

'So what happened to Sergeant Penfold?' Clementine asked quietly. 'Was this before or after Sergeant Penfold went missing?'

'Before,' he murmured. His voice was barely a whisper now; they had to lean in to hear what he said next. 'From what I know, he was busy working on another case and didn't join the rest in their drink. Janice got Maria out all right, but he had worked out where they had gone and took after them after he'd called the ambulance for the rest of the squad.'

'But he didn't manage to arrest them at the hotel?' she asked again. Trying to get the conversation out of George was like trying to get blood from a stone.

'That part I don't know about,' George said. 'Honestly, Maria and Janice ran off into the fields and I didn't see them again that night. Not until, well, I saw Janice a few days later and she didn't look very good at all. She seemed like she was in shock. Obviously, they were already looking for the police officer and I put two and two together. They'd already come for the car and found it in the car park. Colin nearly went down for that one. He's never been able to control his temper.'

'What about Maria?'

He chuckled again and wiped the sweat from his brow with the handkerchief. 'One day not that long ago, probably two or three years ago now, I got a postcard. Which wasn't unusual in itself because I often get postcards, from pen pals and friends back home.' Margery and Clementine nodded, and Margery thought of the large collection of them in his caravan. 'Though they must get bored of me sending them the same postcard of St Martin's all the time! Anyway, this one was from Belgium, which was very exciting in itself and it said something like, "with love from your old friend Mia. Would love to catch up, here's my email".'

'So, that was...'

'It was Maria! Not very covert, but that's Maria. It's amazing she's managed to be away so long really. A big risk for her to try and get in touch, but the first thing she asked was how Thomas was. I think the not knowing had been getting to her over the years.' George smiled at the memory. 'We've been in touch ever since; we video call at least once a month! Due another one, really, but obviously I didn't take my computer with me. It's back at the hotel.'

Clementine sank to the steps and slumped down next to him in shock.

'You've known where she is the entire time?' Clementine demanded.

'I thought you might be most upset by this information.' He smiled at her gently. 'I can see the resemblance between you.'

'But we don't know if I'm related to her,' Clementine spat. 'I wish people would stop assuming I am. What if I'm not? Why get my hopes up when it might not be true?'

'You can still find out.' Margery patted her shoulder gently. 'We could still talk to Thomas about it.'

'Or we could talk to Maria ourselves,' Clementine said. 'Can you put us in touch with her, George?'

'I should think so.' He nodded.

George and Clementine sat together on the step and Margery considered them both.

'She's alive,' Clementine said softly. Her eyes were gazing at a spot on the floor, her thoughts a million miles away from here. She put her head in her hands, looking slightly shellshocked.

'Colin looked for her. Of course he did, but he never thought twice about the postcards I was getting from around the world,' George said in explanation.

'So, he never questioned it?' Margery asked.

'Never.' George shrugged. 'Some people don't want to see these things, though, preferring to live in the dark.'

'Why stay working for Colin?' Margery questioned. 'If he's so horrible?'

George smiled at that. It looked very out of place in the middle of the tense conversation they were having. 'It's not that bad and I have free room and board and the work is not hard. Also, you forget that back when Maria disappeared, I still needed him to sponsor my visa. You're also forgetting that Janice went back to her life, got her daughter to lie for her to give her an alibi. She could have run with Maria, but she stayed for the sake of her daughters, more than anything, and then her grand-daughter after that. Anyway, this'll all be over soon, won't it?'

'Do you think so?' Margery asked. She was not convinced that it was over at all; in fact, it seemed like it might just be beginning.

'They've made an arrest, have they not? Prue seemed to think they'd arrested Emily, but I can't see what for.'

'What do you mean?' Margery asked. 'They think she killed the mayor.'

'Emily?' George said. 'Why would Emily poison the mayor?'

'They said she poisoned Mr Warrell with tea,' Clementine told him.

He looked up at her sharply. 'Mr Warrell has been poisoned?' George's eyes widened. 'What tea?'

'The teas she's always making him,' Clementine said. 'Turns out she's been poisoning Mr Warrell for ages; that's what the police think, anyway.'

George's brow furrowed. 'Are you sure the police said that?'

'Quite sure.' Margery nodded. 'Why?'

'Emily isn't the one who made the teas,' he said. 'Thomas did.' George scratched his head. 'I saw him adding dried plants to them in the kitchen; he always goes out foraging for things now. Janice took him out a few times and showed him what plants were edible when he first started courting young Sophie.'

'Well, would Emily have known Janice Hornbottom?' Margery asked him.

'No, I don't think so, not really.' His voice was full of confusion. 'Why would you ask that?'

'Because she's been poisoned too.'

'Are you being serious?' George's mouth had fallen open in shock.

'Yes.' Margery and Clementine nodded.

'I don't know how Emily would know her.' He rubbed his head again. 'I can't see why she would poison her.'

'Well how long have Sophie and Thomas been seeing each other?' Clementine had found her voice. 'Because that's who the tea was sent to.'

'Sophie?' George shook his head. He looked absolutely shocked. 'Not that long, but surely he wouldn't…?' He trailed off.

'Margery, do you not find it a bit funny that Thomas knew all about what had poisoned his dad?' Clementine asked her.

Margery thought about it; she had not considered it before, but Clementine was right. 'Yes, and Sophie's his girlfriend. Surely he could have given her the tea that nearly killed Janice?'

George leaned back against the stairway he was sitting on, as if it would help him stay upright. They all seemed to have come to the realisation at the same time. 'Yes, and I used to lend him books all the time; he said he was developing an interest in foraging after the walks with Sophie – oh my!'

He stared down at the ground, his eyes opening so wide Margery worried for a moment that they might pop out of their sockets. 'Good Lord, you don't think he would have ever read Maria's diary? It was on my bookshelf with all my other gardening books; he's borrowed lots of them!'

'Maybe? But why start poisoning people?' Margery began to pace; it helped her think. 'But if he'd poison his own father, then I suspect he'd have no problem poisoning Janice or Nathan. Why would he kill Nathan? That's the bit we can't work out.'

'I think I know,' George gasped again, leaping from his seat. 'Gosh, oh gosh, it's all so clear now! I've suspected something was afoot at the hotel for a while, you see; bookings have been unfulfilled, money going missing – it was like there was some inside sabotage. Mr Warrell has been worried about income for a while now.'

'Is that why he was trying to sell it to the mayor?' Clementine asked.

George looked too shocked to say anything, but he nodded vigorously as though all of a sudden a thousand jigsaw puzzle pieces were slotting themselves together in his head. 'Gosh, maybe Thomas was the one cooking that evening! Of course Mr Warrell would cover that up; it makes sense. I just assumed that Emily must have been, but Thomas cooks all the time now!'

Margery gasped.

'So, what will we do about it, detectives?' George asked, smoothing the wisps of black hair over his scalp.

Margery and Clementine shared a look.

Chapter Twenty-Two

Margery felt a horrible stab of déjà vu as they arrived back at the hotel, and with barely any plan at all. She parked the car, with trepidation rising in her chest. This was all going so wrong. The last week had been a complete mess. What was supposed to be a fun summer holiday trip had turned overnight into a never-ending nightmare. They had rung Gloria on the way to let her know what was going on and to check up on Ceri-Ann, who was reportedly back to her normal self. Gloria had not thought it was a good plan and Margery was beginning to agree with her as the minutes ticked by.

Somehow, Janice was still alive, on a ventilator. Sophie had sent a text message to tell them, but it had also been confirmed as hemlock poisoning, just as Janice had thought. She remained hanging between life and death; it remained to be seen which one would be chosen as her fate.

They all stepped out of the car and Margery and Clementine hesitated as George shuffled immediately towards the hotel reception. Clementine had rung Detective Penfold on the way over and tried to explain the situation, and she had demanded that they should not enter the building under any circumstance. Margery was concerned that the whole thing sounded mad. For all they knew there was a perfectly reasonable explanation for all of this.

Maybe Emily had accidentally poisoned Janice and Colin, and Thomas had nothing to do with it. Something told her that was untrue, though. They were about to find out.

George didn't heed Detective Penfold's advice and rushed straight into the hotel, disappearing from sight. Margery decided rashly that he couldn't go it alone, and they followed him inside. The reception was dark, very dark, the only light coming from the computer screen behind the desk. Margery took Clementine by the arm as George led them through the building. The entire building was under a heavy gloom of silence, almost oppressive to Margery's ears; the creaking of the dining room door opening as George turned the handle was nearly enough to make her jump out of her skin. It was still and empty, just as it had been the last time they had been here, all the tables ready and laid out for dinner. They wandered through the dark restaurant and over to the bar in the corner.

'What now?' Clementine whispered. George looked around the room quizzically.

'I think we should go to the flat and see if Thomas is even here,' he said. 'It's possible he's already left.'

'I think we should go outside and wait for the police,' Margery said; Clementine murmured in agreement. 'They said they were on their way.'

'Okay,' George agreed. He strode back across the room; Margery and Clementine followed. George exited into the reception and Margery made to close the dining room door behind them.

'Why are you all here?' a voice came from behind them, and Margery froze. She turned in panic. Thomas looked at them quizzically from the door to the kitchen. Both his arms were behind his back, as though he were trying to hide something. 'We've shut the hotel for the day.'

'Thomas, what have you done?' George gasped, turning back into the dining room. Thomas looked as though someone had just told him he wasn't getting any Christmas presents this year.

'George, what are you doing here?'

'We've come to stop you from killing anyone else!' George yelled. Thomas flinched as George stormed back into the dining room, his finger raised in accusation.

'Get away from me,' Thomas said coolly as George advanced towards him. Margery realised what he had been hiding behind his back as he swung it around to face George, who flinched and held his hands up in shock, his mouth dropping open in surprise.

'Thomas!' George stared at the gun in his hands. 'Please don't!'

There was a bang; Margery froze, closing her eyes with terror instinctively. The noise seemed to reverberate all around the walls of the dining room. There was a scream, and she opened her eyes. What she saw made her nearly slam them shut again. Thomas was standing over George, who was wailing and clutching his foot where the force of the gunshot had knocked him to the floor. Thomas stared down at him, his hands trembling under the weight of the gun in his arms. It was not Colin's shotgun, but the gun Margery had seen in the photograph that Nathan's wife had posted on Facebook and that the mysterious forager had been looking at them with on the fields. She was sure of it. It even had the seagull engraving on the butt.

Thomas's face had turned ashen, almost as if he could be ill at any moment, but he raised the gun and pointed it at them anyway. On the floor, George groaned, the blood from his foot seeping out from underneath him and staining the polished wooden floor. George moaned in pain, trying to grasp for his foot, the shoe he was wearing barely covering the damage and his face turning a horrible pasty white. There was so much blood, the sight of it turned Margery's stomach.

'Margery, isn't it? And Clementine?' Thomas said. He was seemingly jovial, but Margery could not see any joy in his eyes, his voice far too shrill. 'I wasn't expecting to see you again so soon.'

'We weren't planning on coming back.' Margery heard herself answer as if she were speaking in an entirely different room to her ears, or she were answering from underwater.

'Probably would have been better if you didn't.' Thomas shrugged.

'Quite,' Margery replied.

'I don't want to shoot you too, but you haven't really left me much choice, have you?'

Margery felt Clementine grasp for her hand; they began to back instinctively towards the door they had come through. George kept rolling around the floor in pain, groaning and clutching at his injury, and Thomas pointed the gun at him again. Margery saw him take a big deep breath and close his eyes.

'Don't!' she cried, but the gun flashed as the bullet left the barrel. George fell back against the hard floor, crumpling under the force of the bullet. The hole in his shoulder began to stream with blood, his arms limp by his sides. Clementine tugged on her arm but she couldn't look away, her own eyes glued to George's face; he looked as surprised as she felt, his mouth open grotesquely wide and his eyes far away and unseeing. Clementine tugged her again and they began to run.

—

They didn't make it far before Thomas was upon them. They had barely made it out of the reception before he was rushing after them, crashing through the front doors as they made it to the car. Margery's fingers scrabbled in her bag for the keys, cursing herself as she did so.

'I can't find them, Clem, I can't find them!'

Clementine didn't wait to see if they would turn up. Instead, she grasped Margery by the sleeve again and they began to run through the car park with Thomas hot on their tails. He fired at them several times but missed each shot. Margery heard the glass on her car windscreen smashing as they made it to the back of the car park and hit the gate that led to George's caravan.

George. Margery couldn't stop seeing his body crumple to the ground after Thomas shot him.

She caught a glimpse of Thomas as Clementine threw the gate open. The only reason he hadn't killed either of them yet was because he was over by the hotel still, struggling to reload the stolen weapon. Sheer panic overtook her; her limbs felt like she was trying to pull herself through mud, the fear seizing them and making them heavy. They struggled past the caravan and out into the field behind it. They hadn't been this way before on their walks and Margery wasn't sure where the tiny, narrow footpath would take them. She kept her eyes on the horizon as their feet smashed into the soft ground. Clementine's breathing grew more erratic as they hurried, and Margery hoped she wouldn't need her inhaler. Before she had time to worry about that, they reached the end of the fenced-off field and struggled through another gate, out onto a dead end.

Worse than a dead end, Margery thought as they stopped dead before the drop off the cliff, nothing but the open sky above them and nothing but the sea far below them. The waves angry white lines crashing against the cliff edge. Clementine took her hand again and they turned just in time to see Thomas arrive in front of them.

'It was all Emily,' Thomas yelled, panting at the exertion of the chase. 'Didn't the police tell you?'

'They told us what they thought had happened, yes,' Margery shouted back. 'But I must admit, you shooting George has really raised my suspicions of you.'

Thomas grappled with the gun again, and Margery found herself using the second he was distracted to try to find a way out of the situation. She came to the conclusion that there was none just as quickly. Clementine seemed to have come to the same realisation; she was gripping Margery's hand as tight as a vice. Thomas finished reloading, a glimmer of triumph in his eyes for a second, but it disappeared as quickly as it had arrived.

'I didn't mean to kill him; I really liked George.' He was almost tearful. Margery wondered what on earth could have made him feel he had no choice but to do this.

'Well, why did you kill him?' Clementine asked. 'You could have just turned yourself in and he would have been fine! Or better still, not have done any of this in the first place!'

'It's too late for that, isn't it? It's his fault anyway!' he spat. 'I found my mum's diary in George's things last year when I was borrowing his gardening books and then I started digging into what happened. I got Sophie to find me all the articles from that time; my mum wouldn't have done any of that but I realised who she was talking about in the diary – Janice. It was obvious to me.'

'We read it too; we agree with you – we know Maria wasn't the poisoner!' Margery cried. She worried her lip with her teeth. 'You don't have to do this, Thomas!'

'I don't have a choice now, do I! It's too late,' Thomas said, raising his chin defiantly. 'She was my mum; he should never have kept the diary from me! He should have told me about her.'

Now that was something Margery could agree with.

'I knew that Dad would defend me so I thought the best thing I could do was get vengeance for her, revenge for George hiding the diary, and revenge for Arthur not telling me he's my real father.'

'You know Dr Bell is your father?' Margery asked incredulously. 'How?'

Thomas looked quite pleased with himself. 'I had to get to know Janice for that, she obviously knew who "Artie" was, but I had to win her trust.'

'How did you manage that?' Clementine asked coolly. 'Surely not with your glowing personality.'

He ignored the taunt. 'It wasn't hard; I just offered to assist her on her foraging trips. It wasn't a problem for me – in fact it was interesting. She showed me loads of stuff.' He fiddled with the gun again; Margery's eyes were drawn to his finger on the trigger. 'She said that her first rule of foraging was to learn which things might kill you.' He laughed. 'You know the funny thing is that I didn't really put it all together until she told me she taught my mum everything she knew. She was always "Maria this, Maria used to that". It took me a while, but I worked out what Janice must have done. The house she sold, all Mum's visits to her, her revenge on Dad. It all made sense that she was the poisoner, but she didn't know where Mum had gone. Maybe that was for the best – I don't know.'

'What did you do when you realised the doctor was your biological father?' Margery asked. 'Did you tell him you knew?'

'I asked him to do a paternity test.'

'He agreed?' Clementine asked.

'Yep.' Thomas's hands trembled as he held the gun. 'I thought for a bit that maybe we would get to know each other, but then he made me promise not to tell his kids or his ex-wife. Anyway, where had he been when I was growing up? Just left me to it, didn't he? So, I decided when he came to dinner I would kill him in the same way everyone thought my mother killed those people and then George would get the blame.'

'They swapped the plates,' Margery suddenly realised, thinking back to that terrible evening. 'That's why he knew someone was trying to kill him.'

'Yeah, they swapped the plates and the mayor died.' Thomas's chest heaved in panic. 'I didn't mean for that to happen; Arthur was supposed to die.'

'All the same, can you not stop now?' Margery gestured with the hand that wasn't in Clementine's to the gun in his own. 'What will killing us get you?'

'I can't escape if you aren't dead.' His lips were pinched. Margery's eyes flicked back to the gun. 'Why didn't George tell me he had her diary?'

'I don't know,' Margery said.

'You seem to know everything else.'

'I don't think Maria wanted you to know she was alive. She probably swore him to secrecy. How will you find her now that you've killed him?' Margery said and then wished that she hadn't. Thomas's eyes flashed with anger.

'She's alive?' He put a hand behind his head and took a step backward, gasping for air. 'What do you mean, alive?'

'She's...she's...' Margery stuttered, realising what she had just done.

'Well, doesn't matter, does it; she hasn't been here, has she?' he yelled. His face was contorted in rage, like he was simply wearing a twisted Halloween mask of the young man they had met the week before. 'Didn't even try to take me with her.'

'I don't think it was like that at all,' Margery said as soothingly as she could. 'She didn't want to leave you; she said as much in the diary.'

'Maybe.' Thomas kicked at the grass with his toe. 'How would you know?'

Margery's brain was still working overtime thinking of how they could disarm him. They could not hope to physically take the gun from him. He was much younger and stronger than either her or Clementine for that to work, but she lived in faith still that she might be able to talk him out of killing them or in the very least distract him enough until the police arrived.

'That's Nathan Jenkins's gun,' Margery said finally.

'And what if it is?' Thomas laughed darkly. 'He's not using it, is he?'

'Well, no,' Margery said. 'You put a stop to that, didn't you? Why him?'

'I told you it was a mistake!' Thomas laughed again but there was a nervous tone to it, and he looked away from her. 'I took it a few weeks ago after I visited with Dad and saw it, needed a gun. Just in case the plants didn't work on Arthur. Lords-and-ladies isn't that poisonous if you realise something's wrong and stop eating it before your throat closes up, but I had to use it because that was what Janice used to poison people originally. The gun was my back-up plan.'

'Why did you send the poison to Sophie?' Margery asked. 'Were you trying to kill her too?'

'No, of course not.' Thomas looked scandalised. 'She's a nice girl. But she hates tea and her grandma loves it; I knew that Janice would eventually drink it. Playing the long game, see?'

'Why did your dad cover for you?' Margery asked. 'And you nearly killed him; I don't understand…'

'That was hard.' Thomas seemed genuinely conflicted. He took a step back, but his fingers were still tightly wrapped around the gun, his finger white on the trigger as if longing to squeeze it. 'I've been poisoning him with little amounts for months.'

'Why?' Margery exclaimed. 'You were really going to kill him?'

'That wasn't the plan at first.' He shook his head. 'I was just going to give him enough to make him ill so he'd hand the hotel over to me. It didn't take much for Emily to let me in on her herbal tea business; I offered to pay for all the expenses, and then I just added things to the teas she gave him. The sicker he got, the more tea she made him drink; bit of a believer in home remedies is Emily.' Margery and Clementine stared at him open-mouthed. 'So really she's been the one poisoning him.' He nodded as if trying to convince himself it was true. 'But then he started talking about selling the hotel to Nathan and retiring, and I couldn't have that. Where would I go?'

'You'd have got another job, surely?' Margery said. 'Without needing to poison anyone!'

'Why should I?' He sneered. 'That's my inheritance. Anyway, I went to school with Emily. It's so embarrassing that we're basically the same age.'

'Why on earth would you kill him?' Clementine asked. 'Even if he's not your biological father, surely he's raised you all these years?'

'Did you not read Mum's book?' Thomas glared at them both. 'He's the reason she's gone!'

'I don't think that's true; do you really believe that?' Margery found herself asking, looking down the barrel of the gun as he stepped forward again. It did not look high calibre enough to kill them, but she did not want to find out what it could do. George had certainly come off the worst for it from across the room. She had not intended to find out what would happen if it were shot at even closer range.

This was the end, she thought to herself meekly. Finally, this was their last few hours. She had always wondered how she would die and if it would be painful. She supposed she might be about to find out, and she was not looking forward to it. For a moment, regret began to surface to the top of her mind, swimming along among her fear. She needn't have bothered lecturing Clementine for smoking so much before she quit years ago, not when she knew now that they were going to die here on the cliffs, in a strange village they had never visited before, and not of emphysema. She needn't have worried so much about the kitchen ordering or whether they had enough peas for lunchtime. What did all that matter now? She hoped for a second – hope flickering on in her head briefly – that Dawn wouldn't mind taking in a few more cats. She thought of Pumpkin and Crinkles, and whether they would wonder why Margery and Clementine had never returned.

'I don't know,' Thomas said after a beat, through gritted teeth. It looked as though it was physically painful for him to admit what had gone wrong with his plan.

'Sounds like you just wanted someone to blame,' Clementine said.

'So, you've been planning this for a while, have you?' Margery asked; it seemed alien to her. She couldn't imagine ever trying to hurt someone she loved, even if they had turned out to be not quite who you had thought they were.

'Yeah, I've been letting bookings go or doing stupidly cheap dates. Dad's been going mad with worry about it. Can't work out why our profit in the restaurant is so bad.' Thomas lowered the gun a little and Margery could see how smug he looked. 'It's because I kept going in and throwing things away, or breaking things. I took the capacitor out of the freezer. Five grand's worth of stock, gone!' He laughed again. 'He fired the old chef after that one.'

'But why the poison?' Clementine asked. 'It just seems like so much work. Not to mention evil!' Thomas smiled genuinely.

'The poisoner thing is such a huge deal around here, as you know by now,' he said. 'After I read Mum's diary, I decided I'd try and replicate it.' Thomas's face fell a bit. 'Sophie never cared about me anyway. She was happy to print all her little articles about my mum, wasn't she? Never cared about my feelings.'

Poor Sophie, Margery thought. Thomas seemed to have lost even the little bit of control he had over the situation, and he did not seem to know who to aim the gun at any more, between them. Margery winced each time he swung it to face her.

'You don't care if your own dad dies?' Margery gasped.

'It's taken me a while to plan; I had to do it in a way that wouldn't be too painful.' Thomas said. 'What do you take me for?'

'You were on the fields wearing her coat,' Margery suddenly realised.

'Yeah,' he said. 'I was hoping someone would see me and think it was her. Lucky you were around.'

Margery and Clementine took a moment to process this new and startling information. Thomas looked between them coldly, as though deciding what to do next.

'People will look for us,' Margery assured him.

'Yes, we're supposed to be organising a hen party for a very bossy person,' Clementine said. 'She'll look for us. Even if it's just to tell us we've done the wrong colour cakes.'

Thomas looked bemused at that, but he stepped forward again. Margery and Clementine backed away.

There was a yell from behind them all and Detective Penfold appeared across the other side of the field; she was not alone. Thomas stared for a moment and then seemed to make up his mind, aiming the gun at them again and pulling the trigger. In that split second, Margery braced herself, but the gun had jammed and he rushed forward to try again. She looked around to find somewhere to run, but there was nowhere. In front of them were Thomas and the gun; behind them, the edge of the cliff and the water below. The tide was high and the drop did not look as far as she imagined it usually would, but the waves were vicious, slamming against the cliff face. Thomas was so close, in front of them both, the trigger clicking as he tried and tried again to get it to work. The gun finally went off with a bang and Margery found herself losing her footing as the bullet whizzed past her head, staggering backward and grabbing Thomas by the sleeve of his jacket automatically as she went.

She heard Clementine scream her name as she fell, her hands grasping wildly, falling through the air as though she weighed nothing more than a feather until she hit the hard water and pain rushed through all of her limbs as she was sucked into the freezing cold sea feet first.

The longest time a person had ever held their breath was just over twenty-four minutes. Margery did not know why that thought had come into her head, or where she had learned the fact, not when every other thought seemed to be swirling to black as she struggled on upwards. She wondered if she would make even a minute before the water claimed her, her fingers turning to ice. The cardigan that she had picked out carelessly that morning was now a millstone around her neck, full of water and weighing her down as the current took her, her hair swirling up around her head. She opened her eyes, but there was nothing but the darkness of the ocean and the saltwater to burn them and she didn't know which way was up. She kicked frantically and one of her comfortable sandals slipped off her feet and disappeared into the depths below. She did not see it go. She was too busy grasping for the surface above her with desperate, reaching fingers that were so heavy she could barely move them.

Chapter Twenty-Three

Clementine put the newspaper down on the table next to Margery's bed and sat back again, her arms on the arms of the chair and her hands balled up into fists. Margery didn't say anything, had not said anything since she had fallen two days before. Clementine was beside herself. She sat and watched Margery's chest rise and fall, the machine attached to her beeping steadily, her leg in plaster raised above the bed by supports. Clementine kept watching the clock tick above the hospital bed, the knuckles on her hands turning white as they gripped the chair. It was not the first wedding anniversary that she'd had planned for them. The card and the crochet hooks with Margery's name embossed on them were still wrapped up at the bottom of her suitcase, waiting for their owner to be ready for gifts once more.

'Any change?' Rose asked, she slipped into the room quietly and closed the door.

'Still checking for pulmina...pulmonary...oh what's it called?' Clementine struggled with the pronunciation. 'Fluid in the lungs.' Rose hummed quietly and sat down in the chair on the other side of the bed. 'But the doctor seemed very positive. No hypothermia.'

Rose gave her a weak smile and Clementine returned it, not bothering to keep up their faux hatred of each other. She wondered briefly how Rose had managed to get back into the room, how many hospital staff she would have had to argue with to get there. It was barely the crack of dawn, after all, and definitely not visiting hours.

It almost hurt to look at Margery too closely. Her face was sallow, lit by the single strip light running behind the bed and the red tinge of the sky through the window outside, unnaturally white and covered in cuts and bruises. Clementine reached out and stroked her pale fingers instead, careful not to touch the heart rate monitor on her finger. Watching Margery disappear from the cliff edge had been the worst moment of her entire life, worse than anything, even the police dragging out her limp, lifeless body with her leg bent the wrong way from the sea. Clementine couldn't think of anything that would ever be worse than that either. Her own personal super volcano, her own mass extinction event. She didn't want to cry in front of Rose, but when she looked up, Rose looked teary-eyed too.

'I'm going to cancel my hen,' Rose said. She looked very determined in the low light of the machines. 'And the wedding if needs be.'

'You won't,' Clementine said. 'Margery would be livid if you did that; she's been planning the sandwich fillings for months.'

'I'll postpone it, then,' Rose said, just as stubbornly, her lip curling into a sneer.

'How long for?' Clementine scoffed. 'You're getting married in about six minutes, aren't you? Mr Barrow's probably getting his suit ironed as we speak.'

'I'm postponing it,' Rose said, 'and there's nothing you can do about it.'

'What about the billion people you've got coming to your house?'

'They can sleep in the tent!'

'And James?'

Rose leaned forward and leaned her elbows on the bed, looking at Margery with more sorrow and concern than Clementine had ever seen her manage when she was acting a scene for a school production. 'He'll feel the same; she's his favourite dinner lady. Anyway, he loves me – he'd wait regardless.'

He did love her, Clementine thought to herself, it was obvious he did.

She wished that she had told Margery that she loved her more; she was realising now that she often took her for granted. Margery was the calm one with the level head, letting Clementine run riot because she found it amusing. Clementine just went trundling off into the next chaotic misadventure, dragging Margery along behind her without asking her how she felt about anything. She had been so selfish for years, she thought, balling her hands as tightly as they could go, her fingernails leaving indents in her palms. If they had left all this well alone then Margery would be asleep next to her safely in bed and they would be going for dinner in the evening to celebrate their wedding anniversary. Instead of saying any of that to Rose and revealing how she really felt, though, Clementine's brain told her to make a stupid remark, as it usually did.

'Can you get him to cancel the inevitable school assembly he's going to do about this?' Clementine asked. 'Do something fun instead? Read a Roald Dahl poem or something?'

Rose tutted but ignored her. They fell into a comfortable silence.

'Did they find her bag?' Rose asked.

'No, all her knitting's gone,' Clementine sighed, 'and her crochet things. I'll buy her new ones. Once she wakes up.' She said it in as determined a manner as she could muster, like if she said it enough it would be true.

'A real triple threat.' Rose chuckled. 'She could knit, crochet and sew.'

'She still can,' Clementine snapped.

'Yes,' Rose said, wide-eyed. 'Yes, of course she can.'

–

Clementine woke with a start still sitting in the chair, her hand still on Margery's and another on her own shoulder. She flinched it away. Rose was asleep in the chair opposite, her hair mussed up and her face free of make-up. She looked almost an alien species compared to the stern deputy head who usually stalked the halls of Summerview Secondary School.

'Sorry,' Gloria said. 'I just thought you might want to change clothes and have a coffee?'

Clementine wiped the sleep from her eyes and sat up straight, stretching as she did so. She took the cup of coffee from Gloria gratefully and accepted the bag of clothes too.

'I'll look after her while you're gone.' Gloria smiled softly. Clementine nodded and stood from the chair, letting Gloria sit down.

'Thanks, Gloria.'

Clementine wandered out into the hall with the bag and looked around for a bathroom or changing room she could use to quickly change clothes. Instead, she bumped into George, who was limping slowly down the hallway the other way on crutches, his shoulder so heavily bandaged it was almost comical.

'George!' Clementine cried, almost rushing the man as he struggled with his shot foot. 'You're alive!'

'Yes!' He guffawed with laughter and Clementine found herself almost smiling for the first time in days. 'How is Margery?'

'She's not awake yet but they think she'll be okay,' Clementine said, the half-smile instantly wiped from her mouth.

George grimaced at her. 'I'm sorry.'

'She was lucky,' Clementine said, 'as these things go. The tide was going the right way; she washed straight up on the rocks.'

'Yes,' he agreed. 'Very lucky. The officer told me that you tried to jump in after her.'

'Well, yes...' Clementine said. 'Of course I did.'

'Well, I'm glad you didn't.' George gave her that small smile again. 'So Margery didn't have to share her luck.'

'I'm going to...' Clementine raised the bag of clothes Gloria had given her to show him, and pointed it in the general vicinity of the exit door to the hallway.

'Wait,' he said, reaching out for her. 'If Margery's still asleep then I have someone you need to meet, if you want to?'

Clementine almost dropped the bag as she stared at him. He gestured with his head back down the hallway and, cautiously, she followed behind him as he slowly made his way back to the room.

—

He ushered her into the hospital room and then looked back out into the corridor to make sure they had not been followed. George had obviously been here for the same amount as time as they had while he recovered judging by the big tomes about gardening resting on the bedside table, and the get well soon cards. On the table on wheels over the bed rested an old laptop that looked as though it had seen better days.

'Prue brought me some things, so I emailed Maria. She said I can call her,' he whispered. 'Would you like to talk to her?'

Clementine could feel herself going green. She had almost forgotten about Maria, too wrapped up in her worries about Margery to think about her. Anyway, Margery was her family; did she really need anyone else trying to slot themselves into her life? She wished Margery were here to help her decide what to do. Clementine had spent her entire life not knowing anything about her birth family. This might be her only chance. She decided out of pure curiosity to see what Maria had to say. If she thought they might be related too. It had stuck Clementine as funny, when they had found out Maria had been the chef, that she had gone into catering for a career as well. A different type of catering than Maria had, evidently, but still. Maybe there was something in their blood.

George smiled and went to the laptop, gesturing her to follow him and for Clementine to sit in the chair to the side of the bed. He manoeuvred the table to her with great difficulty and slowly set up the video call. He was almost as bad at using computers as Margery or Clementine by the looks of things, but after a moment the call was ringing out. George sat down on the other side of the bed, mirroring the seats Clementine and Rose had chosen early that morning. Clementine felt her hands growing sweaty and she put them in her lap so George could not tell.

Finally, from somewhere across the world, Maria Glover answered.

'George?' she said, squinting at the screen. 'Oh…you're…Clementine?'

'Hello,' Clementine said. There was a pause.

'Oh my God,' Maria breathed. 'He wasn't joking when he said we looked alike, was he? I thought I was looking at my reflection in the screen for a second then!'

There was a definite twang to her accent, though Clementine obviously did not know what she had sounded like when she had lived in St Martin's. She studied her face. They would have still looked very much the same, if it hadn't been clear that Maria dyed her hair. It was still as dark brown as the day the mugshot on the front of the paper had been taken, though it was all pinned back under a red bandana.

'We certainly do.' Clementine chuckled. 'I think I'm a touch better-looking, though!'

They smiled at each other through the screen. It was odd, Clementine thought. She felt like she knew her already.

'I bet you have some questions?' Maria asked.

'I do, a lot of them.' Clementine nodded. 'What time is it there?'

'Oh.' Maria laughed. 'I meant about what happened before, but cr…it's just gone nine.' They fell into an awkward silence as Clementine looked at the clock above the hospital bed.

'Where are you now, then?' Clementine asked. 'You can't be far; it's just gone eight here.'

Maria leaned back in her chair. Clementine could not tell much of her surroundings by the limited scope of the video, but it almost looked like she was sitting at the table in a caravan. The big windows to the side of her looked out at what appeared to be a holiday camp.

'I'm in France at the moment,' Maria said, after a pause. 'For now, so don't go telling the police or anything. Not that they'd be able to find me here; there's hundreds of holiday camps on this bit of coast and it's the right time of year for it. If anyone ever gets suspicious of me, I just move.'

'I'm not going to tell the police,' Clementine said. 'I was just surprised.'

'It's Mia now, by the way.' Maria grimaced and looked around nervously. 'Mia Vincent, just an English holidaymaker travelling about in my caravan, doing the odd catering job here or there. You can call me Maria, though, I suppose.' She got up and Clementine could hear her closing a door.

'Do you travel alone?' Clementine asked.

'Yeah, it's easier that way,' Maria said with a grimace. 'Sometimes I make friends but then we all end up moving on again. It's better not to let anyone get too close…'

It sounded very lonely, Clementine thought. Especially as she and Margery were inseparable. Margery's period of unconsciousness was the longest they had gone without speaking for over forty years. She couldn't imagine sitting alone in a caravan and moving every few weeks to avoid capture.

'We really do look alike, don't we?' Maria chuckled darkly, looking at Clementine's face. 'George said everyone seems to think we're related. I wonder if we should find out.'

'I've been wondering that too,' Clementine agreed, though if she really thought about it she had been deliberately distancing herself from Maria in her head, wishing she could go back to a time before she knew about her. Then she wouldn't have to think about any of it and she could pretend she wasn't intrigued that there might be others, people who she might have called parents if things had been different.

'We could do a DNA-testing kit or something like that, I suppose?' Maria suggested.

'We could,' Clementine said. 'I suppose we should, really. Would you mind?'

'No,' Maria said. 'It would be good to know. So, you don't know anything about your birth parents?'

'Nothing,' Clementine replied. 'You don't know anything at all?'

'My birth mother was from Devon and she got pregnant accidentally. She wasn't married so she gave me up, didn't think she had a choice. She wrote me a letter. I don't have it now, though, obviously, and Colin probably got rid of it years ago. I grew up in Cornwall, bounced about from foster place to foster place till I was eighteen and that's about it.' Maria made a face that said it all quickly, distilling the years down to nothing. 'You?'

A letter, Clementine thought. Maybe she had been given a letter too, as a baby. She was sure her mother would have given it to her though; she had never made it a great secret that she had adopted Clementine. She had always told her that it made no difference to how she felt about her and Clementine had never had any reason to believe any differently.

'My mum adopted me when I was a baby and she was living in Cornwall and then we moved to Dewstow.'

'Huh, I've never been to Dewstow.'

'Well, maybe you can visit,' Clementine told her.

'Even though I'm stuck here?'

Clementine grimaced. 'Maybe not.'

'I suppose you want to know a bit about Janice and what happened?' Maria broke the silence that was threatening to prevail before it could take hold. 'You certainly worked it out before I did.'

'We've…I've heard a lot about Janice, and from Janice,' Clementine said. 'She's been poisoned.'

'George told me.' Maria sighed and took a swig from the glass of wine next to her on the table. 'So, you've got a copycat, have you? I was very interested to hear when George said. Do you know who they are?'

'Well…the police thought it was Emily…' Clementine began, before pausing and wondering if Maria had any idea who Emily was. Maria waved her hands in dismissal.

'I know all about Emily, don't worry.' Maria smirked, raising an eyebrow and pouring herself another glass of wine from the bottle next to her.

'Well, it wasn't her,' Clementine said. 'It was Thomas.'

Maria stared at her, not realising that she had frozen until the wine overfilled the glass and poured onto the table. 'Oh shit.' She jumped up and appeared a moment later, dabbing at the liquid with a tea towel. 'Shit,' she said, sitting back down and throwing the tea towel away from her. 'Not my Thomas?'

Clementine nodded. 'Did you ever talk to him?' she blurted out before she could stop herself.

'No,' Maria said, taking another gulp of wine. It ran down her fingers and dripped from the stem of the glass. Clementine winced at the sight of it; it was too much like the blood that had poured from George's wounds.

'Colin doesn't know you're alive either?'

'No, he doesn't,' Maria said, her eyes wide as though Clementine had asked if she ever tried to get in touch with the dead. 'And I'd prefer it to stay that way. Much too painful to speak to Thomas, or Colin, I'm afraid. It's better to pretend that he doesn't exist, though George will tell me the odd story.' Maria still looked haunted by what she had had to do to stay free. 'I had to run; they would have put me away for a long time, after all those deaths. I had no choice.'

'But Colin wasn't Thomas's biological…'

'Colin loves Thomas,' Maria said firmly. 'And he loved me. It never mattered to him who his biological father was. As far as Colin was concerned, Thomas was his son and the birth certificate said so. It was his idea; he said he could look after us.'

Clementine of all people could understand what Maria meant by that. Even if they didn't share blood, her mother had been her mother, and her brother was her brother, and no one could ever take that from any of them. When she thought of her family, she didn't see the nameless people who had donated their DNA, but her mother sitting in her favourite chair in her garden, sketching the birds as they visited the hanging feeder. Or her brother and her niece visiting as they did every few years and going for dinner and for day trips. She felt the uncertainty, which had been battling in her mind since she had seen the photograph of Maria, begin to rest for a moment.

'So, Dr Bell…?'

'A mistake,' Maria said. 'Just a stupid mistake that went on far too long and ended far too messily.'

'Thomas knew about him,' Clementine said.

'Did he?' Maria put her elbows on the table and leaned her head on one of her hands. 'Did he tell you that?'

'Did Janice ever tell you what she'd done?' Clementine changed the subject, thinking of Janice's pale face after she had made her confession to Margery.

'When she came to get me out.' Maria shrugged. 'Felt guilty, I reckon. She was my closest friend here. I knew she hated Colin, but I never thought she'd do anything to hurt me.'

'Would you not be able to clear your name, now that Janice has confessed to the police?' Clementine asked. 'Start again?'

'I...I don't know,' Maria said, after a long pause. 'I don't know how I'd get back, for one thing. I snuck over here in a car boot, and I don't have a passport or any way to get one, just been sneaking over borders for twenty-odd years. So, probably not without facing retribution, and anyway...' A dark wave seemed to cross her features and her eyes stared, seemingly without seeing them any more. 'I wasn't completely innocent.'

'What do you mean?' Clementine breathed, staring at the computer screen. She saw George freeze from where he had been half listening in the chair.

'There was a police officer. He came after us.'

'I know about Detective Penfold's uncle,' Clementine said.

'He was a Penfold too, yeah.' Maria squinted as she tried to remember his name. 'Yes.'

'She had it out for us when we got here.'

'I'm not surprised, you wandering in, wearing my face.' Maria gave her a small, sad smile. 'Probably thought I'd turned back up to finish the job.'

'Wait, so...how did he die?' Clementine said, turning to look at George, who looked as shocked as she felt. 'No one knows.'

'I assumed that he fell,' George whispered; all the colour had drained from his face. 'What do you mean, Maria?'

'It wasn't intentional, you've got to believe me,' she said, her eyes wide. 'He grabbed me and was trying to handcuff me, but I got away and I ran to the edge of the cliff. He ran after me and tripped and fell off the ledge.' She took in a deep breath and continued. 'But he had hold of the grass and was swinging there.' She stopped for a moment, and her voice dropped. Her eyes looked far away. 'I stood on his fingers so he'd let go.'

'All these years, I believed he had fallen.' George looked completely amazed by the revelation. 'But you murdered him!'

'We had to get away,' Maria said. 'I didn't have a choice.'

Her eyes were blank and lifeless, as though she had been considering what she could have done differently for the past few decades. How different it all could have been. Clementine wondered how on earth she could have ever left her son, how she could have gone this long fighting the urge to contact him. She didn't have any children, but she could not imagine never seeing Margery's face again, could not imagine how much trouble Maria must have felt she was in to abandon her own child. Sitting in front of them onscreen, Maria did not look like the years had done her any good at all. She looked drawn and much too thin, her skin too jaundiced to be healthy. Clementine wondered if it had been worth it; surely a spell in prison could not have been worse than being completely alone.

'There is always a choice,' George said quietly. He left the room, staggering out on his crutches and closing the door softly behind him.

'I didn't have one,' Maria said, just as gently.

They sat in an awkward silence for a minute, Clementine processing the new information, trying to work out what she would have done in Maria's place. For one thing, Margery was always there to stop her executing any of her plans that seemed too hare-brained. Clementine thought that if she were in Maria's shoes, she probably would have reappeared a week later rather than face never seeing Margery's face again. She remembered Margery's poor bruised and broken body, lying a few rooms over, and a chill ran down her spine.

Maria smiled a small, sad smile and Clementine felt guilt set in.

'Listen, Maria…there's something else,' she began.

Maria looked intrigued. 'Oh?'

'Yes.' Clementine didn't know where to start but she knew she had to tell her, even though she wasn't sure she was the right person to. Clementine thought George might have already done it, but it was obvious he hadn't. Maybe he didn't know himself, though he must have heard Colin wailing in grief from the room across the corridor as she had.

'Thomas is dead.'

'What?'

'He drowned.'

Maria stared off into the distance, her hands over her eyes. Clementine wondered if she were thinking about the Thomas that they had seen in the photograph at the Warrell flat. She wondered if she had even seen a photo of him as an adult. How she felt that her son was a murderer. If it even bothered her – after all, she was one too. Something shifted in Clementine's chest. If she was related to Maria, then she was also related to Thomas, the man who had pushed the love of her life off a cliff. She was not sorry that he was dead. She tried but she couldn't bring herself to feel sympathy for Maria either. Not after what had happened. She had killed Detective Penfold's uncle and then run without facing the consequences, and Thomas had nearly done the same to Margery.

'How?' Maria's voice was very small.

'He fell off the cliff too,' Clementine whispered. 'They couldn't save him.'

He hadn't been anywhere near as lucky as Margery had. George was right about Margery having the monopoly on luck. Instead of being spat out onto the rocks as she had, Thomas had been dragged under the waves by the current and his body had been found hours later by the coastguard. She had already been at the hospital with Margery. Detective Penfold thought that the combination of Thomas's thick coat and heavy hiking boots hadn't helped him. He had been sucked away by the tide before anyone could do anything about it.

Maria looked lost, as though she didn't know what to think any more.

–

Her head was buzzing with thoughts, all of them muddled as she walked back down the hall to return to Margery. Maria was alive and well. Maybe not happy, judging by how much wine she had drunk during their brief conversation, but alive definitely. They had swapped email addresses, but Clementine didn't know if she would ever contact her again. If someone had told Clementine at the beginning of the summer holidays that any of this would happen, she would have laughed in their face. A murder, several gunshot wounds, a potential sister, and her wife falling from a cliff face were an unprecedented sequence of events she hoped never to see again. She sucked in a deep breath at Margery's door, her fingers on the handle. Margery's face falling in slow motion, her outstretched arms grasping at the air playing on repeat in her mind. Her fingers slipped from the door handle as it opened from the inside of the room. Rose stood in the doorway, her eyes gleaming.

'I was just coming to find you,' she said. Clementine looked past her into the small room. 'She's awake!'

Chapter Twenty-Four

'Then what happened?' Detective Penfold asked. Margery watched the digital tape recorder as it counted the seconds.

They were sitting once more in the police station interview room, looking across at the two officers who had been so accusatory a few weeks before. Today was the day she had finally been given the all-clear to return to Rose's. A bit battered and bruised and with cuts on her face that were still healing, but alive and back up with her right leg still broken, but mending and able to get around on crutches. There were no other broken bones and she had escaped a worse fate, but she could still feel all the aches from her injuries, and she'd have a scar above her eyebrow where she had cracked her head on the rocks.

Margery had never really believed in luck or God or any other sort of helpful entity before, but if there were ever going to be a sign of something else, maybe that was it. She had decided privately to take it easier from now on. Maybe she and Clementine didn't need to go chasing after problems each time they occurred.

'Well, then you got there and arrested him...' Margery began.

'...And Margery flung herself off a cliff,' Clementine finished.

Margery laughed. 'I don't think I'm going to be entering any Olympic diving events anytime soon, do you?'

'I don't know.' Clementine scratched her chin. 'It would have been quite impressive if it wasn't so frightening.'

'Frightening is the word for it.' Detective Penfold nodded. 'Especially as we'd just come across Mr Kale lying on the dining-room floor.'

'I can't imagine him wanting to go back to work there after all that,' Margery said.

Detective Penfold smiled. 'He's not going back; he's retiring. He has some plans to travel around Europe in his caravan.'

Margery smiled at that. She could tell Clementine was thinking about Maria, who George was probably planning to meet on his journey. From what Clementine had said, although George had been livid about Maria's revelation about Penfold's uncle, he had decided to let bygones be bygones for the time being. He had kept her secrets for this long, he had reasoned, and she did seem sorry. At least she wouldn't be alone any more. The way Clementine told the story about their meeting, though full of bluster and drama as usual, Maria seemed desperately lonely and resentful. It was not a life she wished for anyone.

'He was very brave standing up to Thomas like that, as were you. God, there can't be many beds left in the hospital, can there?' Detective Penfold shook her head. 'Though I suppose they didn't have to find one for Thomas.'

'What about Colin and Emily?' Margery asked.

'Colin is still recuperating, and Emily's name has been cleared,' Detective Penfold said. 'Dr Bell is awake too and doing okay. It was touch and go with organ failure for a bit, but he got through it.'

'And Janice?' Clementine asked.

'Janice?' Detective Penfold said, her features darkening for a moment. 'She's alive. She's not well, but she's alive and awake. I don't know for how long.'

'Did she——?' Margery began. Detective Penfold cut her off.

'She confessed to everything,' she said, her face suddenly emotional, though she realised quickly and pulled her features back into their usual position. 'The poisonings, pushing my uncle to his death. Everything. Her house is being searched as we speak. They've found some…interesting things. My mum is relieved we know what happened now. Not that it makes any of it better. I'm not sure if she's going to hold on long enough to be prosecuted.'

Margery couldn't find the words to speak. Janice had confessed to everything, even things she hadn't done. Why would she do that? Perhaps she had decided that, as the entire events of thirty years ago had been her fault in the first place, it was the only way she could fix it on her deathbed.

'Will Sophie be all right?' Clementine asked. 'If her grandmother dies?'

'I think so,' Detective Penfold said. 'She has her job at the paper. I wasn't sure Mr Warrell would let her live in the house any more, not after what her grandmother did, but he's a lot more forgiving than me, said she can stay, and he'd sell it to her. Maybe he feels guilty about Thomas.'

'Oh,' Margery said. 'Well, I suppose that solves that, then. Except her boyfriend trying to kill her grandmother for revenge.'

'Yes, not exactly Boyfriend of the Year material,' Detective Penfold said. 'The other mystery left is what happened to Maria Glover, I suppose.' She gave them a knowing look. 'I think it's safe to say that if she ever did return then it would be safe for her to do so; I told George the same thing.'

For a moment, Margery wondered whether to tell her the entire truth or not, but then she asked herself what good it would do. Clementine had confided in her on their way to the station that Maria had almost certainly decided not to return to the county. She was too used to her runaway lifestyle by now. Margery thought of Maria in her trailer somewhere in France. Maybe she would be able to fix this now if she was in the clear and she changed her mind. She could go to the embassy and come back to the country. Clementine still didn't seem sure about Maria or how she felt about her, and Margery didn't want to press her.

'There's just one more thing that hasn't been cleared up,' Margery said thoughtfully. 'What was all that business at Rose's house with the flowers and the tyres?'

'I'm still working on it,' Detective Penfold said with a huff. 'Nothing new has come up; I'm hoping it was random, perhaps a tourist. Kids playing a joke, maybe.'

Margery was not so sure about that.

'Well, thanks very much, ladies,' Detective Penfold said, as the officers packed up their recording equipment, 'though you'll forgive me if I say that I'm hoping we'll never meet again like this.'

'We feel the same,' Clementine assured her. They stood and let Detective Penfold usher them from the room. Margery took a long time to hobble out on the crutches. They had offered her a wheelchair on loan but she had been determined to get walking again after being bedridden for weeks.

'Next time, maybe just come for the summer fete instead,' Detective Penfold joked as they walked back down the hallway, she a few paces in front of them as Clementine stayed by Margery's side. 'Have a go on the tombola instead.'

Rose and Seren jumped up eagerly from the reception chairs when they appeared in the lobby, along with Nathan's wife, who had been sitting with them. She looked a lot better since they had last seen her, a lot less weepy.

'Hello, Mrs Jenkins,' Margery said. 'How are you?'

'Hello. Fine, fine in the circumstances.' Andrea nodded at both Margery and Clementine. The bags under her eyes were still there, but she looked a lot less distraught than she had. 'I just wanted to thank you for solving Nathan's death. I'm not sure the police could have done it without you. Honestly, you ought to set up a detective agency or something...' Clementine nudged Margery playfully in the ribs at that. 'Thank you.'

'It was no bother,' Margery said, omitting the several dangerous moments they had experienced over the last few weeks. 'No bother at all.'

'Sorry I was so dismissive of you when we met,' Andrea said. 'It was just...well...'

'Quite understandable.' Margery smiled at her.

'Yes, we'd have thought we were lunatics too,' Clementine said.

'Listen, Nathan's funeral is on Friday,' Andrea said, fidgeting with the tissue in her hands. 'The service is family only, but I thought I'd invite you both to the wake. I know it's short notice, but I really can't thank you enough for what you've done.'

'That's actually the day of our friend's hen party.' Margery gestured to Rose. 'She already had to cancel it for me once, so we'll be a bit preoccupied. Honestly, I think the village has probably had enough of us by now!'

Andrea smiled at that. 'Very well, you're welcome if you change your mind, though, honestly.'

'Thank you,' Margery said. They all left the station together, Margery and Clementine trailing behind slowly as Margery gingerly used her crutches. They wandered outside to where Christopher was waiting by Rose's car, smoking a cigarette in the bright sunshine.

Margery stopped in her tracks.

'Are you all right?' Clementine asked in concern, taking her arm. 'What's wrong? Is your leg hurting?'

'Christopher is wearing those boots. Gosh, what were they called?' Margery asked. Clementine looked to see where she was staring and then back at her to see if she'd somehow lost her mind in the past few minutes.

'Yes,' Clementine said, though Margery could tell she was humouring her, 'I'm sure Ceri-Ann could recommend you a pair if you fancy getting some? Maybe for after you get the cast off?'

'No, it's not that. They're those ones, the ones Karen and Sharon like, aren't they?' Margery said, staring at him. 'And that coat, the green coat! The man on the camera was wearing the exact same things, remember?'

Clementine looked again more closely and then took off her glasses so she could see better, joining Margery at squinting over at him across the car park.

'Oh, yes! Look at the yellow stripe on them!' she exclaimed. 'You don't think?'

Margery gasped, 'I do, Clem! Oh my God, we've got to go back in and tell the police.'

'He's the one who smashed all her pots and put those foxgloves on the doorstep? What on earth!' Clementine said. 'And our car tyres!'

'I know! We're going to have to tell Rose; we've got to get her away from him. If he'd do that to one of his friends, then there's no telling what else he'd do,' Margery said. Clementine looked over at Rose in concern. Margery wondered what Christopher had been playing at. But it all made sense now. Of course he would have been able to hide his face on the camera; he was the one who had helped Rose put it up. He knew exactly where it was positioned.

'I'll go and get Detective Penfold,' Clementine whispered to Margery before yelling across the car park. 'Rose! Can you come and give Margery a hand? I forgot my cardigan!'

'Mrs Butcher-Baker! You're wearing it!' Rose yelled back. She exhaled heavily, left Christopher and went to join Margery.

Epilogue

Rose had reacted exactly as Margery had expected her to and Christopher had not been given an easy time by either her or Detective Penfold. Rose had threatened all sorts of horrific tortures and police restraining orders if he ever returned to darken her doorway again, using the full power of her years of drama training to truly make an impact. Detective Penfold swore after that she recognised some of her speech as being from the film *Gladiator*.

Christopher had denied it all at first, but when he realised that the jig was finally up, he confessed. He told the police how he had found out about her divorce and thought that now Rose was single again that they could make another go of it. He hadn't realised until she had arrived for the summer that she was imminently planning to marry Mr Barrow. When confronted about the foxgloves, he had simply said that Rose had always said how pretty they were when they had been courting thirty years before. The weird note had been to symbolise how she used to ask him to rehearse Shakespeare plays with him during her drama studies. Rose denied all memory of any of that, but as he had placed them on the doorstep the day before she'd finally told him about James Barrow, she admitted he was probably innocent of trying to kill them all.

Friday bloomed bright and clear, the sky as blue as far as the eye could see. It was the nicest day so far of the entire summer holiday and perfect for Rose's hen party. None of the dinner lady team got to enjoy the morning, however, as they had spent most of it preparing the food ready for the guests to arrive.

'I wish we'd never agreed to this,' Clementine hissed as she iced the third batch of cupcakes. 'Thank God she went with a proper caterer for the wedding in the end; I don't think I could cope. I don't understand how anyone can be allergic to so many things.'

'Amen,' Gloria said, furiously buttering bread as quickly as she could while Ceri-Ann piled cheese onto a huge platter.

'Gloria, please do not swear!' Clementine hissed. 'This is a very old farmhouse; the ghosts might come for us.'

'Are you feeling better after all that the other week, Ceri-Ann?' Margery asked to distract Clementine. To her shock and embarrassment, she realised she had been so wrapped up in her own injuries that she hadn't asked how Ceri-Ann was at all yet.

'Oh yeah, much better, ta.' Ceri-Ann smiled, beginning to decorate the cheese tower with a generous topping of Branston pickle.

'You recovered very quickly, though,' Clementine said, 'for someone who was convinced they were dying.'

'Yeah, I suppose I did.' Ceri-Ann smiled, adding even more pickle to the already smothered cheese tower. Margery sensed by the unease on her face that there was something more to it. Maybe Ceri-Ann had been hiding a secret of her own for the entire holiday.

'So, what did Dr Bell say?' Clementine asked, nosy as ever.

'Well…' Ceri-Ann took a deep breath, putting the pickle down on the table and turning to look them all in the eye. 'He said I should go and buy a pregnancy test.'

'That sexist pig!' Karen cried from where she and Sharon were doing the washing-up in the massive double kitchen sink. They were both wearing denim hot pants; the rest of the jeans had obviously not made it into shorts in Margery and Clementine's absence. 'He's got some nerve!'

'Yeah!' Ceri-Ann cried, waving her pickling spoon in agreement. 'Only, well, it turns out I am pregnant.'

There was a hushed pause before everyone burst out into noise again.

'Oh, Ceri!' Gloria rushed to hug her with tears in her eyes. 'That's such lovely news!'

Karen and Sharon had already reached her, speedy with their years of marathon training and Ceri-Ann was trying to duck away from their wet washing-up hands as they tried to grasp her into a bear hug.

'Yeah, yeah, yeah!' She flapped their hands away. 'Get off me!' But she was beaming.

'Who's the father?' Karen asked, suddenly suspicious. 'Do we know him?'

'Yeah, I think so.' Ceri-Ann picked up the spoon again. 'Do you know Symon? The police officer?'

'What!' Clementine dropped the icing bag on the floor in surprise. It rolled under the counter with a flump. 'Officer Symon? The most useless police officer in the whole of Dewstow? He's only about twelve, Ceri-Ann! You'll be arrested.'

'He's twenty-six.' Ceri-Ann laughed. 'A perfectly sensible age to be a dad, don't worry.'

'Well, I think it's lovely.' Margery smiled, reaching down to help Clementine clean up the icing sugar she had spilled while she scrabbled underneath the table for the icing bag.

'So do I.' Ceri-Ann beamed again. She put one hand on her still flat stomach unconsciously.

There was a loud bang from somewhere upstairs and the noisy thumping of someone running down them. Seren burst into the room, wide-eyed and in a sweaty panic, an unlit cigarette in her hand. She had obviously been on her way outside for a smoke and been distracted.

'What's wrong, Seren?' Karen asked. 'Have you lost your lighter? I'll pop the toaster on; you can light it off that.'

'I've just seen through…the window!' Seren gasped in short bursts, ignoring Karen and trying to get her breath back. 'Mrs Blossom! She's…here!'

Rose's arch nemesis from rival school Ittonvale arriving was not a good omen; Margery groaned at the drama of it all. Rose had hated her with a vengeance ever since Mrs Blossom had stolen her lesson plan and subsequently the job she had applied for several decades before.

'So?' Clementine asked.

'She wasn't invited!' Seren cried. 'We've got to get her out of here before Rose sees her.'

There was a shriek from upstairs and then they could hear Rose scream Seren's name. Seren rushed back out of the kitchen in a panic.

'Rather her than us, eh?' Clementine nudged Margery. 'At least we're nice and safe in here.'

'For now.' Margery grinned. 'We've got to put the food outside in a minute; I can't wait to see who else came without an invite.'

'Oh God, I forgot about the decorations.' Gloria's eyes widened. 'Look, I did the best I could with the cakes, but I haven't had as much time as I wanted to decorate them.'

'Oh, wow, Gloria!' Margery exclaimed as Gloria tilted the cake tin back and forth to show them the swirly cupcakes inside. 'They're amazing!'

Gloria smiled widely. 'Yes! I'm so glad they worked out. I've never had to do anything so complex before. I think I'm ready to apply for *The Great British Bake Off* now.'

'You can't, mate.' Ceri-Ann shook her head. 'You've got an NVQ in cooking.'

'Well, they'll never know that!' Clementine said. 'And if they come to the school to see if she works in the kitchen, we'll lie and say we've never seen her before in our lives.'

The others laughed and then they all got back to work, the room busy with swarming dinner ladies. Everyone rushed around doing various jobs or carrying food to the trestle tables they had set up outside.

There was a gasp from the kitchen doorway and Margery and Clementine both looked up to see where it had come from. The older woman in the party dress seemed to realise her faux pas, putting the bottle of prosecco and card she was holding in the pile of them on the kitchen counter before turning to them.

'Sorry,' she said, grimacing at Clementine. 'You just look so much like—'

'Maria Glover?' Clementine interrupted her. The woman nodded, wide-eyed. 'Yes, I get that a lot. Don't worry.'

She scuttled away and Margery and Clementine shared a look.

'Have you thought any more about the DNA testing?' Margery asked gingerly. Clementine had told Margery that they had left the chat on a good note, but Margery could tell that the entire spectacle had been entirely too weird.

'I've decided not to do it,' Clementine said, returning to the sandwiches, her face set determinedly.

'Oh,' Margery said. 'I thought you weren't sure about it?'

'I wasn't,' Clementine agreed, arranging the finger sandwiches neatly on the tray. 'But I loved my mum, and I don't really want to find out if there's anyone else. Even estranged sisters who've changed their names. And I don't really want to know if I'm related to Thomas; I'm perfectly mad enough without having a murderer for a nephew...or a sister for that matter. Though I suppose Maria's was a bit less planned.'

'I quite understand.' Margery finished adding the last of the cheese and pineapple to the cocktail sticks and stood back from the table to admire her handiwork. 'Some stones are much better left unturned.'

'Indeed,' Clementine said, taking her hand and considering her face. 'Anyway, you're my family. And Crinkles and Pumpkin. And the entire Education Centre Nourishment Consultants team, obviously. Even Rose, even though she's sometimes more like a mad aunt than a friend.'

'Even though Crinkles eats us out of house and home and Pumpkin is always trying to trip us down the stairs? And you tell Ceri-Ann twice a week at work that next time she annoys you you're going to hide her house keys?' Margery smiled; Clementine chuckled and then leaned in to kiss her.

'Of course. But don't tell any of them how much I like them!' Clementine's smile turned into a full grin. 'I've got something for you, actually – wait here.'

She rushed off before Margery could say anything and she could hear her clomping up the stairs. Margery eyed her crutches wryly, wondering where Clementine had expected her to rush off to. She looked around the busy kitchen and peered through the open kitchen doors into the garden, where she could hear the cheerful voices of arriving guests. She closed her eyes for a moment, happy to be here, happy to not be dead, happy to exist in their little world again.

Clementine crashed back into the room, jolting her from her thoughts, her arms full of gifts.

'Clem?' Margery said weakly. 'What's all this?'

'Happy belated anniversary! Don't worry, not a foxglove in sight.'

She handed the flowers over. Margery took them and smelled them.

'Oh, they're lovely, Clem! Gosh, I haven't got you anything; it's all gone out the window after all that.' She put the flowers on the table as Clementine tried to hand her the jewellery box. Margery opened it to reveal a delicate gold necklace with a wave of blue as the feature. She gasped at how pretty it was.

'Don't be silly,' Clementine said, taking the necklace from the box and moving around her to put it on her neck. 'You deserve it. I bought it in Merrowpool yesterday when you were buying Dawn some rock to thank her for looking after the cats.'

'Oh, it's lovely, Clem,' Margery said, touching the chain and smiling at herself in the mirrored surface of the oven doors opposite.

'Thought it might remind us of our holiday. Though, now I think about it, we might want to forget it. You nearly dying again, a load of other people dying.' Clementine chuckled. 'Gosh it really wasn't that great a time at all.'

Margery joined her, turning to kiss her.

'Well.' She smiled as she put her hands on Clementine's shoulders. 'At least we won't forget our first wedding anniversary!'

They carried their last trays out of the kitchen through the kitchen back door and outside to where Gloria was arranging them all neatly on the tables. It was a fantastic spread if Margery did say so herself. They had really outdone themselves this time. Sandwiches, snacks and picky bits were laid over two tables and then they had even managed to pull off an entire table just for desserts. Sharon had made a fabulous trifle and it sat next to the strawberry meringue roulade and Gloria's cupcakes. The savoury food did not look too bad either; there were three types of savoury quiche and even homemade Scotch eggs that Clementine had whipped up. Margery could not have been prouder of her catering team.

The guests were beginning to arrive and were being ushered into the back garden through the large open gate by Gary Matthews, Seren's boyfriend. He had obviously come down for the day to help. The back garden itself was a rambling sprawl as far as the eye could see. Rose had told her a few nights ago that her grandfather had owned all the land surrounding the property at one point, but she'd sold some of it off to pay for parts of her divorce. Margery could not imagine how ridiculously large the amount of land had been for her to still have so much garden, front and back of the house. Seren rushed out through the kitchen doors, her eyes wild and panicked still.

'She's coming!' she cried. The dinner lady team took their places as the guests milled around. Along with Mrs Blossom, Margery could see Elle Macdonald, one of the English teachers, next to Mrs Boch, the librarian. Even Mrs Mugglethwaite had somehow managed to wangle herself an invite along with her cohort of ladies she usually travelled on the bus with. Doreen Rolley was over by the ornamental fountain, sipping a glass of champagne from the tray that Sharon was offering around, wearing what was obviously her smartest pair of dungarees. There were a few visitors from the village too, including the woman who had been so shocked by Clementine, though Margery could not have named any of them. It seemed that Rose was much more liked than she had ever thought.

Rose arrived in the kitchen doorway, and they waited with bated breath as she took it all in. Waiting to see what she would find fault with as the soundtrack from *Les Misérables* blared from Ceri–Ann's portable Bluetooth speaker. Her eyes scanned the colourful bunting and the table of delicate finger sandwiches and cakes, the tablecloth blowing gently in the light breeze. Bottles of champagne on ice sat on the table next to an array of gold-rimmed coupe glasses.

Rose nodded approvingly at it all. Margery felt Seren and the rest of the dinner lady team release the breath they had all been holding. Mrs Blossom rushed over to greet Rose with open arms; her tiny Yorkshire terrier, Mrs Ada Bones, bounced around her feet excitedly. Rose's smile fell for a moment at the sight of the long white dress Mrs Blossom was wearing, but then reappeared with gusto, even the annoying presence of a former rival unable to ruin the party under the warm breeze of the lovely garden and the summer sun.

Acknowledgements

Here we are again! As always, there are so many people to thank and not enough space – thank you as always to all my family and friends, but especially to Mum and Jim, Dad and Kirsty, Becky, Rachel and Bethan.

Thank you to Francesca, Thanhmai and everyone else at Canelo and Canelo Crime, with an especially big thank you to my long-suffering editor, Siân Heap. Thank you for the massive amounts of work you put in making these stories publishable!

Thank you to Matt and Chepstow Bookshop for all your support with books one and two – when my sisters and I used to queue for midnight Harry Potter releases I never even imagined seeing my books stocked in the shop, a dream come true! Similarly, thanks to Kevin Norris and Alouisa Jones from The Works Abergavenny for inviting me into store to sign copies of book two, you made me feel so welcome.

A big thank you to City of Bristol college in entirety, but especially to chef lecturer Ryan Fernandes for organising the CPD day on foraging and to Desmond Smith for his many ideas for horrible murders in ongoing books, some much worse than others!

To my wife Robyn, thank you for everything you do. Thank you for letting me blab at you to work through various bits of storyline, for not letting me kill off all the main characters like I keep threatening to and for doing loads more than your fair share of the housework, so I have the time to do this.

Last but not least – thank you to you for reading! These books only exist because of you, and I am eternally grateful to anyone who reads them. It's been lovely to get to know some of you on Instagram and I really hope you enjoyed Margery and Clementine's latest adventure!

Until next time!

CANELOCRIME

Do you love crime fiction and are always on the lookout for brilliant authors?

Canelo Crime is home to some of the most exciting novels around. Thousands of readers are already enjoying our compulsive stories. Are you ready to find your new favourite writer?

Find out more and sign up to our newsletter at canelocrime.com